Teacher Reference Handbook

Macmillan McGraw-Hill

Math Connects

2

Macmillan/McGraw-Hill

The *McGraw·Hill* Companies

 Macmillan/McGraw-Hill

Send all inquiries to:
Macmillan/McGraw-Hill
8787 Orion Place
Columbus, OH 43240-4027

ISBN-13: 978-0-02-107523-2
ISBN-10: 0-02-107523-9

Grade 2 Teacher Reference Handbook

Printed in the United States of America.

6 7 8 9 10 RJE 15 14 13 12 11

Teacher Reference Handbook

Contents

Scope and Sequence

Number and Operations	PreK	Kindergarten	Grade 1	Grade 2	Grade 3	Grade 4	Grade 5	Course 1	Course 2	Course 3	Pre-Algebra	Algebra 1	Geometry
Whole Numbers													
One-to-one correspondence	●	◐	●	●	●	●	●						
Count, read, write, name, rename, represent Numbers to 10	◐	◐	●	●	●	●	●						
Numbers to 30		◐	●	●	●	●	●						
Numbers to 100			◐	●	●	●	●						
Numbers to 1,000				◐	●	●	●						
Numbers to 10,000					◐	●	●						
Numbers to 1 million						◐	●						
Numbers to billions							●						
Skip count			◐	●	●	●	●						
Equivalent Forms (word, expanded, standard)	●	●	●	●	●	●	●						
Place value		●	◐	●	●	●	●	●	●				
Powers and exponents							◐	●	●	●	●	●	●
Negative-integer exponents									◐	◐	●		
Scientific notation										◐	◐		
Round whole numbers			●	◐	●	●	●	●					
Compare and order whole numbers		●	◐	●	●	●	●						
Represent on a number line		●	◐	●	●	●	●	●					
Even and odd numbers, doubles			●	●	●	●							
Factors and multiples					●	◐	●	●	●	●	●	●	
Prime and composite numbers						◐	●	●	●	●	●	●	
Prime factorization						◐	●	●	●	●	●	●	

Legend:
● Introduce   ● Develop   ● Reinforce   ● Maintain and Apply   ● Prerequisite Skills

	PreK	Kindergarten	Grade 1	Grade 2	Grade 3	Grade 4	Grade 5	Course 1	Course 2	Course 3	Pre-Algebra	Algebra 1	Geometry
Greatest common factor (GCF)						◐	●	●	●	●	●		
Least common multiple (LCM)							●	◐	●	●	●		
Perfect squares, cubes, roots								◐	●	●	●	●	●

Fractions

	PreK	Kindergarten	Grade 1	Grade 2	Grade 3	Grade 4	Grade 5	Course 1	Course 2	Course 3	Pre-Algebra	Algebra 1	Geometry
Model fractional parts of a whole, of a set or group	●	●	◐	●	●	●	●	●	●	●			
Read and write fractions		●	◐	●	●	●	●	●	●	●	●	●	●
Represent fractions on a number line				◐	◐	●	●	●	●	●	●	●	●
Compare and order fractions			◐	◐	●	●	●	●	●	●	●	●	●
Equivalent fractions				◐	◐	●	●	●	●	●	●	●	●
Simplify fractions					●	◐	◐	●	●	●	●	●	●
Least common denominator (LCD)							◐	●	◐	●	◐	●	●
Reciprocal, multiplicative inverse								◐	●	●	●	●	●
Mixed numbers and improper fractions						◐	●	●	●	●	●	●	●
Relate fractions and decimals					●	◐	●	●	●	●	●	●	●

Decimals

	PreK	Kindergarten	Grade 1	Grade 2	Grade 3	Grade 4	Grade 5	Course 1	Course 2	Course 3	Pre-Algebra	Algebra 1	Geometry
Model decimals					●	◐	●	●	●	●	●	●	●
Read and write decimals					◐	●	◐	●	●	●	●	●	●
Represent decimals on a number line						◐	●	●	●	●	●	●	●
Compare and order decimals						◐	●	●	●	●	●	●	●
Round decimals						◐	●	●	●	●	●	●	●
Terminating and repeating decimals								◐	●	●	●	●	●
Non-repeating decimals/ irrational numbers												◐	●

Scope and Sequence

Number and Operations

Ratio, Rate, Proportion

Ratio, Rate, Proportion	PreK	Kindergarten	Grade 1	Grade 2	Grade 3	Grade 4	Grade 5	Course 1	Course 2	Course 3	Pre-Algebra	Algebra 1	Geometry
Concept of a ratio							●	●	●	●	●	●	●
Model ratios							●	●	●	●	●	●	●
Read and write ratios							●	●	●	●	●	●	●
Relate ratios to fractions							●	●	●	●	●	●	●
Rates							●	●	●	●	●	●	●
Unit rate							●	●	●	●	●	●	●
Rate of change								●	●	●	●	●	●
Direct variation							●	●	●	●	●		
Ratio and probability							●	●	●	●	●		
Solve proportions							●	●	●	●	●	●	●
Proportional reasoning							●	●	●	●	●	●	●
Scale drawings								●	●	●	●	●	●
Scale factor								●	●	●	●	●	●
Similar figures							●	●	●	●	●	●	●
Indirect measurement								●	●	●	●	●	●
Dilations											●		●

Percent

Percent	PreK	Kindergarten	Grade 1	Grade 2	Grade 3	Grade 4	Grade 5	Course 1	Course 2	Course 3	Pre-Algebra	Algebra 1	Geometry
Concept of percent, model							●	●	●	●	●		
Relate fractions and decimals to percents							●	●	●	●	●		
Percent of a number							●	●	●	●	●		
Percent one number is of another								●	●	●	●		
Percent proportion ($\frac{P}{B} = \frac{R}{100}$)								●	●	●	●		

● Introduce ● Develop ● Reinforce ● Maintain and Apply ● Prerequisite Skills

	PreK	Kindergarten	Grade 1	Grade 2	Grade 3	Grade 4	Grade 5	Course 1	Course 2	Course 3	Pre-Algebra	Algebra 1	Geometry
Percent equation ($RB = P$)								◑	●	●	●		
Percent of change								◑	●	●	●		
Interest, profit, discount								◑	●	●	●		

Integers

	PreK	Kindergarten	Grade 1	Grade 2	Grade 3	Grade 4	Grade 5	Course 1	Course 2	Course 3	Pre-Algebra	Algebra 1	Geometry
Concept of integers, negative numbers							◓	●	●	●	●	●	●
Read and write integers							◓	●	●	●	●	●	●
Represent on a number line							◓	●	●	●	●	●	●
Compare and order integers							◓	●	●	●	●	●	●
Absolute value								◑	◑	◑	●	●	●

Rational Numbers

	PreK	Kindergarten	Grade 1	Grade 2	Grade 3	Grade 4	Grade 5	Course 1	Course 2	Course 3	Pre-Algebra	Algebra 1	Geometry
Identify and simplify rational numbers								◑	●	●	◑	●	
Represent on a number line								◑	●	●	●	●	
Relate rational numbers to decimals								◑	●	●	◑	●	
Compare and order rational numbers								◑	●	●	●	●	

Real Numbers

	PreK	Kindergarten	Grade 1	Grade 2	Grade 3	Grade 4	Grade 5	Course 1	Course 2	Course 3	Pre-Algebra	Algebra 1	Geometry
Identify irrational numbers									◑	●	●	◑	●
Represent irrational, real numbers on a number line									◑	●	●	◑	●
Identify and classify real numbers									◓	●	●	●	●
Estimate square roots									◑	●	●	●	●

Scope and Sequence

Number and Operations

Understand Operations	PreK	Kindergarten	Grade 1	Grade 2	Grade 3	Grade 4	Grade 5	Course 1	Course 2	Course 3	Pre-Algebra	Algebra 1	Geometry
Model, meaning of addition	●	●	◐	●	●	●	●						
Model, meaning of subtraction	●	●	◐	●	●	●	●						
Meaning of multiplication: repeated addition, equal groups, arrays				◐	◐	●	●						
Meaning of division: equal groups, repeated subtraction				●	◐	●	●						
Inverse operations: relate addition and subtraction; multiplication and division			●	◐	◐	●	●						
Check subtraction by adding				◐	●	●	●						

Operations: Whole Numbers	PreK	Kindergarten	Grade 1	Grade 2	Grade 3	Grade 4	Grade 5	Course 1	Course 2	Course 3	Pre-Algebra	Algebra 1	Geometry
Add whole numbers Basic facts	●	●	◐	◐	●	●	●	●	●	●			
Fact families		●	◐	●	●	●	●	●	●	●			
Count on, doubles			●	●	●	●	●						
Number line			●	●	●	●	◐	●	●	●			
Algorithm (regroup), partial sums			●	◐	●	◐	●	●	●	●			
Three or more addends				◐	●	●	●	●	●	●			
Subtract whole numbers Basic facts	●	●	◐	●	●	●	●	●	●	●			
Fact families			◐	●	●	●	●	●	◐	●			
Count back			◐	●	●	●	●	●	●	●			
Number line			◐	●	●	●	●	●	●	●			
Algorithm (regroup)			●	◐	●	◐	●	●	●	●			

● Introduce   ● Develop   ● Reinforce   ● Maintain and Apply   ● Prerequisite Skills

	PreK	Kindergarten	Grade 1	Grade 2	Grade 3	Grade 4	Grade 5	Course 1	Course 2	Course 3	Pre-Algebra	Algebra 1	Geometry
Multiply whole numbers Basic facts				◐	◐	●	●	●	●				
Fact families, related facts				◐	◐	●	●	●	●				
Multiply three numbers					◐	●	●	●	●				
Algorithm (regroup)				◐	●	●	●	●	●				
Divide whole numbers Basic facts				◐	●	●	●	●	●				
Fact families, related facts				◐	●	●	●	●	●				
Algorithm					◐	●	●	●	●				
Remainders					◐	●	●	●	●				

Operations: Fractions

	PreK	Kindergarten	Grade 1	Grade 2	Grade 3	Grade 4	Grade 5	Course 1	Course 2	Course 3	Pre-Algebra	Algebra 1	Geometry
Add and subtract fractions and mixed numbers Like denominators							◐	●	●	●	●	●	
Unlike denominators							◐	●	●	●	●	●	
Multiply and divide fractions, mixed numbers								●	●	●	●	●	

Operations: Decimals

	PreK	Kindergarten	Grade 1	Grade 2	Grade 3	Grade 4	Grade 5	Course 1	Course 2	Course 3	Pre-Algebra	Algebra 1	Geometry
Add and subtract decimals Money amounts					○	●	●	●					
Non-money amounts					◐	●	●	●	●	●	●		
Multiply decimals						○	●	●	●	●	●		
Divide decimals						○	●	●	●	●	●		

Operations: Integers, Rational, Real Numbers

	PreK	Kindergarten	Grade 1	Grade 2	Grade 3	Grade 4	Grade 5	Course 1	Course 2	Course 3	Pre-Algebra	Algebra 1	Geometry
Add and subtract integers								◐	●	●	●	●	●
Multiply and divide integers								◐	●	●	●	●	●

Scope and Sequence

Number and Operations	PreK	Kindergarten	Grade 1	Grade 2	Grade 3	Grade 4	Grade 5	Course 1	Course 2	Course 3	Pre-Algebra	Algebra 1	Geometry
Rules of exponents								◐	●	●	●	◐	●
Add, subtract, multiply, and divide rational numbers									◐	●	●	●	●
Add, subtract, multiply, and divide real numbers												◐	●

Mental Arithmetic and Estimation Strategies	PreK	Kindergarten	Grade 1	Grade 2	Grade 3	Grade 4	Grade 5	Course 1	Course 2	Course 3	Pre-Algebra	Algebra 1	Geometry
Add and subtract multiples of powers of 10			○	●	●	●	●	●	●				
Multiply multiples of powers of 10				◐	◐	◐	●	●	●				
Divide multiples of powers of 10					◐	●	●	●	●				
Use addition properties						◐	●	●	●				
Use compensation						◐	●	●	●				
Estimation	◐	◐	●	●	●	●	●	●	●				
Rounding			○	◐	●	●	●	●	●				
Estimate sums			○	◐	●	◐	◐	●	●	●	●		
Estimate differences			○	◐	●	●	◐	●	●	●	●		
Estimate products					◐	◐	●	●	●	●	●		
Estimate quotients						◐	●	●	●	●	●		
Use compatible numbers, clustering					○	◐	●	●	●				
Estimate with fractions								◐	●	●			
Estimate percents								◐	●	●	◐		
Estimate square roots								◐	●	●	●	●	●

● Introduce   ● Develop   ● Reinforce   ● Maintain and Apply   ● Prerequisite Skills

Algebra

Legend: ● full ◐ partial ○ introduced

Use Patterns

	PreK	Kindergarten	Grade 1	Grade 2	Grade 3	Grade 4	Grade 5	Course 1	Course 2	Course 3	Pre-Algebra	Algebra 1	Geometry
Sort and classify by attribute	○	◐	●	●	●								
Identify, describe patterns	○	○	◐	●	●	●	●						
Extend patterns	○	◐	●	●	●	●	●						
Create patterns	○	○	◐	●	●	●	●						
Number patterns			◐	●	●	●	●						
Use addition and subtraction patterns				◐	●	●	●						
Use multiplication patterns					◐	●	●						
Use division patterns							◐						

Properties

	PreK	Kindergarten	Grade 1	Grade 2	Grade 3	Grade 4	Grade 5	Course 1	Course 2	Course 3	Pre-Algebra	Algebra 1	Geometry
Associative and Commutative Properties			○	●	●	●	●	◐	●	●	●	●	
Identity Properties			○	◐	●	●	●	◐	●	●	●	●	●
Zero Property of Multiplication				◐	●	●	●	●	●	●	●	●	●
Distributive Property					◐	●	●	◐	◐	◐	●	●	
Order of operations					◐	●	◐	◐	●	●	●	●	●
Addition and Subtraction Properties of Equality								◐	●	●	●	●	◐
Multiplication and Division Properties of Equality								○	●	●	●	◐	◐
Additive Inverse Property								○	●	●	●	◐	●
Multiplicative Inverse Property									◐	●	●	●	●
Closure Property												◐	●
Properties of equalities and inequalities												◐	●

Scope and Sequence

Algebra

Algebraic Representations	PreK	Kindergarten	Grade 1	Grade 2	Grade 3	Grade 4	Grade 5	Course 1	Course 2	Course 3	Pre-Algebra	Algebra 1	Geometry
Write and solve number sentences using symbols, +, -, =		●	●	●	●	●	●						
Missing addends or factors			●	●	●	●	●						
Variables, expressions, equations					●	●	●	●	●	●	●	●	●
Order of operations						●	●	●	●	●	●	●	●
Evaluate algebraic expressions						●	●	●	●	●	●	●	●
Write algebraic expressions and equations					●	●	●	●	●	●	●	●	●
Use formulas					●	●	●	●	●	●	●	●	●
Inequalities with variables									●	●	●	●	●
Equivalent expressions; simplify expressions								●	●	●	●	●	●
Monomials									●	●	●	●	●
Operations with monomials									●	●	●	●	●
Polynomials, definition										●	●	●	●
Operations with polynomials										●	●	●	●
Factor polynomials												●	●
Pythagorean Theorem								●	●	●	●	●	●
Distance formula									●	●	●	●	●
Radical expressions												●	●
Rational expressions, algebraic fractions											●	●	●

● Introduce   ● Develop   ● Reinforce   ● Maintain and Apply   ● Prerequisite Skills

Solve Equations and Inequalities

	PreK	Kindergarten	Grade 1	Grade 2	Grade 3	Grade 4	Grade 5	Course 1	Course 2	Course 3	Pre-Algebra	Algebra 1	Geometry
Addition and subtraction equations					○	◐	●	●	●	●	●	●	●
Multiplication and division equations						◐	●	●	●	●	●	●	●
Multiple-step equations								◐	●	●	●	●	●
Equations with variables on both sides									◐	●	●	●	●
Solve inequalities									○	◐	●	●	●
Graph inequalities									◐	●	●	●	●
Multiple-step inequalities										◐	●	●	●
Compound inequalities												◐	●
Absolute-value equations, inequalities												◐	
Quadratic equations, graphing and factoring												◐	

Graph Linear and Nonlinear Equations and Inequalities

	PreK	Kindergarten	Grade 1	Grade 2	Grade 3	Grade 4	Grade 5	Course 1	Course 2	Course 3	Pre-Algebra	Algebra 1	Geometry
Relationships between equations and their graphs						○	○	◐	●	●	●	●	●
Linear equations								◐	●	●	●	●	●
Rate of change								◐	◐	●	●	●	●
Slope								◐	●	●	●	●	●
Intercepts								◐	●	●	●	●	●
Slope-intercept form									○	◐	●	●	●
Point-slope form											○	◐	●
Systems of linear equations and inequalities, graph and solve										◐	◐	◐	●

Scope and Sequence **TR11**

Scope and Sequence

Algebra	PreK	Kindergarten	Grade 1	Grade 2	Grade 3	Grade 4	Grade 5	Course 1	Course 2	Course 3	Pre-Algebra	Algebra 1	Geometry
Functions and Relations													
Function tables				◐	◐	●	●	●	●	●	●	●	
Function rules				◐	◐	●	●	●	●	●	●	●	
Definition of function				●	●	●	◐	◐	◐	●	●	●	
Definition of relation, mapping												◐	
Domain and range of functions								●	◐	●	●	●	
$f(x)$ notation									◐		●	●	
Vertical-line test for functions											◐	●	
Identify linear and nonlinear functions, relationships								◐	◐	●	●	●	
Graph ordered pairs					●	◐	●	●	●	●	●	●	
Graph functions						◐		◐	●	●	●	●	
Graph relationships							◐	●	●	●	●	●	
Model real-world data							◐	◐	●	●	●	●	
Proportional relationships, direct variation								◐	●	●	●	●	
Inverse variation									●		◐	●	
Quadratic functions										◐	●	●	
Exponential functions											●	●	
Rational functions												◐	
Absolute-value functions												◐	
Families of linear functions											●	◐	●
Families of nonlinear functions											●	◐	●
Arithmetic sequences								◐	●	●	●	●	

◯ Introduce ● Develop ● Reinforce ● Maintain and Apply ● Prerequisite Skills

Measurement

Length, Weight, Mass, Area, Capacity, Volume

	PreK	Kindergarten	Grade 1	Grade 2	Grade 3	Grade 4	Grade 5	Course 1	Course 2	Course 3	Pre-Algebra	Algebra 1	Geometry
Compare and order	○	○	◐	●	●	●	●						
Nonstandard units	○	○	◐	●	◐								
Customary units			○	◐	●	●	●	◐	●	●	●	●	●
Metric units				◐	●	●	●	◐	●	●	●	●	●
Estimate measurements				◐	●	●	●						
Convert units within a system				○	○	●	●	◐	●	●	●	●	●

Temperature

	PreK	Kindergarten	Grade 1	Grade 2	Grade 3	Grade 4	Grade 5	Course 1	Course 2	Course 3	Pre-Algebra	Algebra 1	Geometry
Temperature (Celsius, Fahrenheit)		○	○	◐	●	●	●	●	●	●	●	●	

Time

	PreK	Kindergarten	Grade 1	Grade 2	Grade 3	Grade 4	Grade 5	Course 1	Course 2	Course 3	Pre-Algebra	Algebra 1	Geometry
Morning, afternoon, evening	○	◐	◐	●	●	●							
Calendar	○	◐	●	●	●	●	●						
Tell time, digital/analog		○	◐	●	●	●	●	●					
Estimate time		○	●	●	●	●	●	●					
Elapsed time				○	○	◐	●	◐					
Order events	○	◐	●	●	●	●							
Units of time		○	○	◐	●	●	●	●					

Money

	PreK	Kindergarten	Grade 1	Grade 2	Grade 3	Grade 4	Grade 5	Course 1	Course 2	Course 3	Pre-Algebra	Algebra 1	Geometry
Recognize and count coins			◐	●	●	●	●						
Compare money amounts			◐	●	●	●	●						
Find values of coins			◐	◐	●	●	●						
Make change					◐	●	●						
Fractions, decimals, and money					◐	●	●						

Scope and Sequence

Measurement

Measurement	PreK	Kindergarten	Grade 1	Grade 2	Grade 3	Grade 4	Grade 5	Course 1	Course 2	Course 3	Pre-Algebra	Algebra 1	Geometry
Measurement Formulas and Techniques													
Use formulas						●	●	●	●	●	●	●	●
Length													
Perimeter of rectangle				●	●	●	●	●	●	●	●	●	●
Circumference of circle							●	●	●	●	●	●	●
Area and Surface Area													
Compare and order areas		●	●	●	●	●	●						
Estimate area					●	●	●						
Area of rectangle, square				●	●	●	●	●	●	●	●	●	●
Area of parallelogram							●	●	●	●	●	●	●
Area of triangle							●	●	●	●	●	●	●
Area of trapezoid								●	●	●	●	●	●
Area of circle								●	●	●	●	●	●
Area of composite figures							●	●	●	●	●	●	●
Surface area of cube, rectangular prism							●	●	●	●	●	●	●
Surface area of cylinder								●	●	●	●	●	●
Surface area of cone, pyramid, sphere									●	●	●	●	●
Volume													
Volume of cube, rectangular prism							●	●	●	●	●	●	●
Volume of cylinder								●	●	●	●	●	●
Volume of cone, pyramid, sphere									●	●	●	●	●
Angle measurement in degrees							●	●	●	●	●	●	●

● Introduce　● Develop　● Reinforce　● Maintain and Apply　● Prerequisite Skills

	PreK	Kindergarten	Grade 1	Grade 2	Grade 3	Grade 4	Grade 5	Course 1	Course 2	Course 3	Pre-Algebra	Algebra 1	Geometry
Precision and significant digits												◐	
Indirect measurement								◐	●	●	●	●	

Geometry

	PreK	Kindergarten	Grade 1	Grade 2	Grade 3	Grade 4	Grade 5	Course 1	Course 2	Course 3	Pre-Algebra	Algebra 1	Geometry
Plane and Solid Shapes													
Identify attributes of plane shapes	○	◐	●	●	●	●	●	◐	●	●	●	●	●
Identify attributes of solid shapes	○	◐	●	●	●	●	●	◐	●	●	●	●	●
Classify and describe properties of plane shapes	○	◐	●	●	●	●	●	◐	●	●	●	●	●
Classify and describe properties of solid shapes	○	◐	●	●	●	●	●	◐	●	●	●	●	●
Relate plane and solid figures	○	◐	●	●	●	●	◐	●	●	●	●	●	●
Lines, line segments, rays					◐	●	●	●	●	●	●	●	●
Parallel, perpendicular lines					◐	●	●	●	●	●	●	●	◐
Classify and measure angles					◐	●	●	●	●	●	●	●	●
Angle relationships								◐	●	◐	●	●	●
Identify and define polygons		○	◐	◐	●	●	●	●	◐	●	●	●	◐
Classify quadrilaterals					◐	●	●	◐	●	●	●	●	◐
Classify triangles					◐	●	●	●	◐	●	●	●	◐
Sum of angles in a triangle								◐	◐	●	●	●	◐
Sum of angles of polygons								◐	●	◐	●	●	◐

Scope and Sequence

Geometry

Geometry	PreK	Kindergarten	Grade 1	Grade 2	Grade 3	Grade 4	Grade 5	Course 1	Course 2	Course 3	Pre-Algebra	Algebra 1	Geometry
Parts of circles								○	●	●	●	●	●
Congruent figures				○	◑	●		●	●	●	●	●	●
Similar figures								◑	●	●	●	●	●
Corresponding parts								◑	●	●	●	●	●
Scale drawings								◑	●	●	●	●	●
Right triangles and parts								◑	●	●	●	●	●
Pythagorean Theorem								◑	●	●	●	●	●
Right triangle trigonometry													◑

Coordinate Geometry

Coordinate Geometry	PreK	Kindergarten	Grade 1	Grade 2	Grade 3	Grade 4	Grade 5	Course 1	Course 2	Course 3	Pre-Algebra	Algebra 1	Geometry
Position and direction	○	◑	●	●	●	●	●						
Graph ordered pairs				○	◑	◑	●	●	●	●	●	●	●
Horizontal, vertical distance on a grid			○	◑	●	●	●	●	●	●	●	●	●
Distance formula										◑	●	●	●
Graph linear equations								◑	●	●	●	●	●
Slope								◑	●	●	●	●	●
Slope-intercept form of line								◑	●	●	●	●	●
Point-slope form of line												◑	●
Slope of parallel, perpendicular lines												◑	●

Transformations and Symmetry

Transformations and Symmetry	PreK	Kindergarten	Grade 1	Grade 2	Grade 3	Grade 4	Grade 5	Course 1	Course 2	Course 3	Pre-Algebra	Algebra 1	Geometry
Translations (slide)							◑	●	●	●	●	●	●
Reflections (flip)							◑	●	●	●	●	●	●

Legend: ○ Introduce ● Develop ● Reinforce ● Maintain and Apply ● Prerequisite Skills

	PreK	Kindergarten	Grade 1	Grade 2	Grade 3	Grade 4	Grade 5	Course 1	Course 2	Course 3	Pre-Algebra	Algebra 1	Geometry
Rotations (turn)					◐	●	●		●	●	●	●	●
Dilations									◐	◐	●	●	●
Transformations on coordinate plane						◐	◐	●	●	●	●	●	●
Symmetry (line and rotation)				○	◐	●		●	●	●	●	●	●
Tessellations						◐	●		●	●	●	●	●

Spatial Reasoning

	PreK	Kindergarten	Grade 1	Grade 2	Grade 3	Grade 4	Grade 5	Course 1	Course 2	Course 3	Pre-Algebra	Algebra 1	Geometry
Draw angles, lines, polygons					○	◐	●	●	●	●			●
Constructions											◐		●
Draw 3-dimensional objects									◐	◐	●		●
Nets					○	●	●	●	●	●	●		◐

Data Analysis

	PreK	Kindergarten	Grade 1	Grade 2	Grade 3	Grade 4	Grade 5	Course 1	Course 2	Course 3	Pre-Algebra	Algebra 1	Geometry
Sort, Classify													
Sort and classify by attribute	○	◐	●	●	●								
Use Venn diagrams		○	◐	●	●	●	●	●	●	●	●	●	◐

	PreK	Kindergarten	Grade 1	Grade 2	Grade 3	Grade 4	Grade 5	Course 1	Course 2	Course 3	Pre-Algebra	Algebra 1	Geometry
Collect, Organize, and Display Data													
Collect data	○	○	◐	◐	●	●	●	●	●	◐	●	●	◐
Organize data with a table			◐	◐	●	●	●	●	●	●	●	●	
Organize data with a graph	○	○	◐	◐	●	●	●	●	◐	●	●	●	
Frequency tables; tally charts			◐	◐	●	●	●	●	●	●	●	●	

Scope and Sequence

Data Analysis

Data Analysis	PreK	Kindergarten	Grade 1	Grade 2	Grade 3	Grade 4	Grade 5	Course 1	Course 2	Course 3	Pre-Algebra	Algebra 1	Geometry
Surveys		●	●	◐	◐	●	●	●	●	●	●	●	
Samples								●	●	●	●	●	
Random samples									●	◐	●	●	
Use sampling to predict								●	◐	●	●	●	

Represent Data

Represent Data	PreK	Kindergarten	Grade 1	Grade 2	Grade 3	Grade 4	Grade 5	Course 1	Course 2	Course 3	Pre-Algebra	Algebra 1	Geometry
Real graphs	●	◐											
Picture graphs, pictograph	●	◐	●	●	●	●	●						
Bar graphs; double bar graphs		●	◐	●	●	●	●	●	●	●	●		
Line plots					◐	●	●	●	●	●	●	●	
Circle graphs								◐	●	●	●	◐	●
Line graphs							◐	●	●	●	●	●	
Stem-and-leaf plots								◐	●	●	●	●	
Box-and-whisker plots									◐	◐	●		
Histograms								◐	●	●	●		
Scatter plots								◐	●	●	●		
Fitted lines on scatter plots								●	◐	●	●		
Choose an appropriate graph/display							◐	●	●	●	●	●	

Make Inferences and Predictions

Make Inferences and Predictions	PreK	Kindergarten	Grade 1	Grade 2	Grade 3	Grade 4	Grade 5	Course 1	Course 2	Course 3	Pre-Algebra	Algebra 1	Geometry
Use data		●	◐	●	●	●	●	●	●	●	●	●	
Mode		●	●	●	●	●	●	●	●	●	●	●	
Median						◐	●	●	●	◐	●	●	
Mean							◐	●	◐	●	●	●	

● Introduce   ● Develop   ● Reinforce   ● Maintain and Apply   ● Prerequisite Skills

	PreK	Kindergarten	Grade 1	Grade 2	Grade 3	Grade 4	Grade 5	Course 1	Course 2	Course 3	Pre-Algebra	Algebra 1	Geometry
Range							◐	●	●	◐	●	●	
Outliers						○	◐	●	●	●	◐	●	
Quartiles											◐	●	●
Misleading graphs and statistics									◐	●	●	●	
Make predictions from graphs						○	○	◐	●	●	●	●	
Make predictions from a sample							○	●	●	●	●		

Probability

	PreK	Kindergarten	Grade 1	Grade 2	Grade 3	Grade 4	Grade 5	Course 1	Course 2	Course 3	Pre-Algebra	Algebra 1	Geometry
Certain, probable, impossible			○	○	◐	●	●	●					
Likely and unlikely, compare likelihoods				○	◐	●	●	●					
Predict outcomes					○	◐	●	●	●	●	●	●	
Outcomes and sample space						◐	◐	●	●	●	●	●	
Probability of a simple event						○	◐	●	●	●	●	●	
Complementary events								◐	●	●	●	●	
Composite events: independent, dependent									◐	●	●	●	
Mutually exclusive or inclusive events, disjoint											◐	●	
Experimental probability						○	◐	●	●	●	●	●	
Theoretical probability						○	◐	●	●	●	●	●	
Probability and ratio								◐	●	●	●	●	
Simulations									◐	●	●	●	
Tree diagrams							◐	◐	●	●	●	●	●
Fundamental Counting Principle							○	◐	◐	●	●	●	

Scope and Sequence

Data Analysis

Data Analysis	PreK	Kindergarten	Grade 1	Grade 2	Grade 3	Grade 4	Grade 5	Course 1	Course 2	Course 3	Pre-Algebra	Algebra 1	Geometry
Combinations						○	○	◐	●	●	●		
Permutations								◐	●	●	●		
Probability distributions											◐		

Problem Solving

Strategies and Skills	PreK	Kindergarten	Grade 1	Grade 2	Grade 3	Grade 4	Grade 5	Course 1	Course 2	Course 3	Pre-Algebra	Algebra 1	Geometry
Look for a pattern	○	◐	◐	●	●	●	●	●	●	●	●	●	●
Act it out, use objects, use simulation		○	◐	●	●	●	●	●	●	●	●	●	●
Guess and check		○	○	◐	●	●	●	●	●	●	●	●	●
Draw a picture or diagram		○	◐	●	●	●	●	●	●	●	●	●	●
Make a table		○	○	●	●	●	●	●	●	●	●	●	●
Make a graph		○	○	○	◐	●	●	●	●	●	●	●	●
Make a list				◐	◐	●	●	●	●	●	●	●	●
Make a model		○		◐	●	●	●	●	●	●	●	●	●
Work backward				○	◐	●	●	●	●	●	●	●	●
Use logical reasoning			○	◐	◐	●	●	●	●	●	●	●	●
Use a four-step plan			○	◐	●	●	●	●	●	●	●	●	●
Choose a strategy			◐	◐	●	●	●	●	●	●	●	●	●
Choose an operation				○	●	●	●	●	●	●	●	●	●
Check for reasonableness			○	○	◐	●	●	●	●	●	●	●	●

○ Introduce   ● Develop   ● Reinforce   ● Maintain and Apply   ● Prerequisite Skills

	PreK	Kindergarten	Grade 1	Grade 2	Grade 3	Grade 4	Grade 5	Course 1	Course 2	Course 3	Pre-Algebra	Algebra 1	Geometry
Write a number sentence			○	◐	●	●	●						
Write an equation						◐	●	●	●	●	●	●	●
Use formulas						○	●	●	●	●	◐	●	●
Decide whether to estimate or compute					◐	●	●	●	●	●	●	●	●
Identify missing or extra information					◐	●	●						
Solve multi-step problems						◐	●	●	●	●	●	●	●
Conduct a poll or survey				○	◐	●	●	●	●	●	◐	●	
Solve a simpler problem					◐	●	●	●	●	●	●	●	●

Mathematical Reasoning and Justification

	PreK	Kindergarten	Grade 1	Grade 2	Grade 3	Grade 4	Grade 5	Course 1	Course 2	Course 3	Pre-Algebra	Algebra 1	Geometry
Use mathematical reasoning		○	○	◐	●	●	●	◐	●	◐	◐	●	◐
Use Venn diagrams		○	◐	●	●	●	●	◐	◐	●	◐	●	◐
Explain, justify, and defend reasoning			○	◐	●	●	●	●	●	◐	◐	◐	◐
Check validity of calculated results			○	◐	●	●	◐	●	●	●	●	●	●
Create problems					◐	●	●	●	●	●	●	●	●
Write informal mathematical arguments				○	◐	●	●	●	●	●	●	◐	◐
Make and test conjectures, counterexamples						○	○	◐	◐	◐	●	●	●
Inductive reasoning								◐	◐	●	●	●	●
Deductive reasoning								◐	●	●	●	●	●
Develop a proof: paragraph, algebraic, coordinate, indirect												◐	●

Literature Support

Contents

Linking to Literacy

The Read-Aloud Anthology is intended to introduce and reinforce the concept(s) being introduced in each chapter of the Student Edition. As you read each selection aloud, model fluent, proficient oral reading. (Students may follow along as you read; text for each read-aloud selection can be found in *Hands-On Activity Tools and Resources*.

The following summaries relate how you might use each section of the teacher support found through the Read-Aloud Anthology in your classroom.

Reading in Math

- Use this section to underscore the relationship between the read-aloud selection for a given chapter and the math concept contained in that chapter.

- The support in this section might also reinforce common reading and language arts skills derived from the chapter's selection. For example, phonemic awareness or phonics skills identified in the piece might be identified and explained to primary students. For upper elementary students, this section might introduce common language arts elements, such as parts of speech or figurative language. You might also use this section to assess students' prior knowledge of the main ideas in the read-aloud piece.

Math Vocabulary

- Use this section to integrate and/or review math vocabulary from the read-aloud selection with the math vocabulary found in the **Student Edition.**

- Most support written for this section refers to the Vocabulary graphic organizer found in *Hands-On Activity Tools and Resources*. This graphic organizer is based on the Frayer Model (Frayer, 1969).

- You might wish to model using this graphic organizer initially, gradually allowing students to complete charts independently later in the year. Primary students will likely use drawings to complete the four fields, while upper-elementary students should use phrases and words to complete theirs. You may wish to have students organize these pages in Math Vocabulary Folders for their reference throughout the school year and as a study guide for spring testing.

Math Comprehension

- Use this section to help students connect comprehension of the read-aloud selection to comprehension of the chapter's math content. This might be in the form of teacher-led discussion, a brief activity, or completion of a graphic organizer.

- Students should be expected to demonstrate familiarity and knowledge of the math chapter's content and connect it through an activity. For example, they might use the Venn diagram graphic organizer to compare two distinct math concepts in a selection, or they could complete the 4-column chart graphic organizer to demonstrate multiple approaches to problem solving.

Literature Support

Reading in Math

Read aloud the poem, *Marvelous* Math, to students, modeling fluent, proficient oral reading.

- Ask the students what kind of sentences they see in the poem. (Sample answer: question sentences) Have the students circle all the question marks in the poem. Count the question marks.

- Ask the students, "Besides question marks, how do you know a sentence is a question sentence?" (Sample answer: question words) List question words.

Math Vocabulary

- Write the word *Mathematics* on the overhead using Vocabulary 1. Ask the students what mathematics is. List all the words the students come up with. (Sample answers: math, adding, subtracting, measuring, telling time…)

- Explain to the students that they are all correct. Continue filling in the graphic organizer.

Math Comprehension

- Partner students up and ask them to *estimate* answers to the questions in the poem. They want to find reasonable guesses.

- Once the students have written answers to most questions gather them together again and have them share their answers. Write a few answers for each question.

- Put the answers on a number line in order from least to greatest.

- Then compare the students' answers to find the most reasonable estimate.

- Then compare the students' answer to find the most reasonable estimate.

Marvelous Math

by Rebecca Kai Dotlich

How fast does a New York taxi go?
What size is grandpa's attic?
How old is the oldest dinosaur?
The answer's in *Mathematics*!

How many seconds in an hour?
How many in a day?
What size are the planets in the sky?
How far to the Milky Way?

How fast does lightning travel?
How slow do feathers fall?
How many miles to Istanbul?
Mathematics knows it all!

Literature Support

Maybe

by Dan Greenberg

Maybe is a funny word
Or maybe not, I guess.
Maybe is sort of *no*
And also sort of *yes*.

Maybe I'll take four plus six
And you'll take six plus four
And maybe when we add them up
Maybe I'll have more.
Maybe.

Or maybe I've got *breakfast*
And *fast break* is what you've got
Backwards, forwards, just the same
Maybe... maybe not!

Maybe you have three and twelve
And I have twelve and three
You say there's a difference?
Maybe I disagree.

Maybe anything going *this* way
Can go *that* way as well
When you ring the *bell door*
I ring the door*bell*.
Maybe.

Maybe it doesn't matter
Which direction you try
Five and nine, nine and five
Hello, *bye good, good bye!*
Maybe.

Maybe this is a *set-up*
Or maybe I'm *upset*
Waterfall or *fall water*
Either way you're wet!

Maybe or *be may*
Be may or *maybe* not
One thing you've got to admit
Fun this poem's a lot!

Reading in Math

Read aloud the poem, *Maybe*, to students, modeling fluent, proficient oral reading.

- Review the th- blend sound.

- Ask students to circle the words with a th- blend throughout the poem. (Sample answers: them, the, three, there, this, that, thing)

- List words from poem and any words the students can name.

Math Vocabulary

- Point out to the students that the poem says the word plus. Review that plus is another way to say add. Ask students another way to say add or plus.

- List the words the students come up with on chart paper.

- Pass out Vocabulary 1 chart. Tell the students to choose one of the words and define it on the chart.

Math Comprehension

- Review the Commutative Property. Explain to students that the numbers can be inversed and the answer will remain the same.

- Have the students look through the poem and underline the addition problems: $6 + 4$, $4 + 6$, $12 + 3$, $3 + 12$, $9 + 5$, $5 + 9$. Ask for volunteers to suggest other addition problems and their inverse. Write them all on chart paper.

- Ask students to write the addition problems and solve them.

Reading in Math

Read aloud the poem, *The Take-Away Cat*, to students, modeling fluent, proficient oral reading.

- Explain to the students that contractions are two words put together to shorten them by *taking away* a few letters. The words are separated by an apostrophe.

- Ask students to circle contractions in the poem. (Sample answers: she'll, she's, it's, can't, didn't, don't)

- Use one of the words from the poem to illustrate writing a contraction (ie: she + will − wi = she'll). Call on students to write the contraction on chart paper.

Math Vocabulary

- Use the VENN Diagram graphic organizer to compare and contrast *addition* and *subtraction*.

- Ask students to tell how the concepts are alike and how they are different.

Math Comprehension

- Ask the students to write their names on a piece of paper. Have them count the letters in their names and write the number of letters underneath their names.

- Explain to them that the *Take-Away Cat* is stealing the vowels from their names. Have them count the total vowels in their names and write that number under the total number of letters. They should subtract the two numbers. (Sample answer: 5 letters - 3 vowels = 2 letters)

- Have the students share their work with the group.

THE TAKE-AWAY CAT

by Dan Greenberg

Gather around so you can hear
About a feline who makes things disappear
When it comes to taking, there's never enough.
She's the Take-Away Cat.
So hide your stuff!
She takes keys, pencils, buttons, mittens,
Watch out for this calico kitten!
That five-dollar bill you thought you lost?
You thought it slipped
Right out of your hand?
Well, guess again—it was the Take-Away Cat!

She'll swipe that smile right off your face
She'll take the buzz right from a bee
The "ten" from *tent* and *Tennessee*
The white off snow
The green off trees
A firefly's glow
The stink off cheese
She'll take away anything she can
Because she's the Take-Away Cat!

Addition? No, she likes subtraction
Taking away is her favorite action
It's what she likes, what she does best
You give her more, she'll hand you less
You give her twelve, she'll take eight
And leave you four to contemplate
You give her nine, she'll take three
You can't object or disagree
She's what she is, understand?
A flabber-grabbin Take-Away Cat!

So pay attention, sit up, listen
If you notice something missing
Don't blame it on your little sister
Because she didn't do it, mister!
Neither did your best friend's cousin
Your uncle's cat? No it wasn't.
You know who it was, you know her game
She'll steal the very letters from your name
Is there ever a moment
When enough's enough?
She's the Take-Away Cat, so hide your stuff!

Reading in Math

Read aloud the poem, *How did you get to School Today?* to students, modeling fluent, proficient oral reading.

- Discuss the poem by listing the ways students could get to school in the poem.

- Collect data with the class on how each of the students gets to school day after day. Display the data on the board for all students to see.

Math Vocabulary

- Discuss the graph using math vocabulary that was introduced throughout the chapter such as: graph, picture graph, data, and survey.

- Display vocabulary words by labeling a large graph that hangs in the classroom.

Math Comprehension

- Have the students fill in a two-column graph illustrating how they go to school. One column should list the various ways students could go to school. Record the number of students who take each mode of transport in the second column.

- Ask questions after the graph is completed. (Sample answers: How many students take a bus to school? Why is the graph not completed for giraffe? How many students were surveyed?)

How did you get to School Today?

by Sheryl Rains

How did you get to school today?
By horse by train, by New York subway?
Did and airplane pick you up from your house?
Did you ride on a sled pulled by a mouse?
I know it sounds silly but I won't laugh?
If you came to school on a giraffe.
Will you add your way to our picture graph?

Reading in Math

Read aloud the poem, *Your Call is Very Important to Us*, to students, modeling fluent, proficient oral reading

- Review compound words with the students. Explain to the students that compound words are like *adding* two words together to get a new word.

- Have the students circle the compound words. (Sample answers: understand, meanwhile, goldfish, something, rattlesnake)

- Model putting the words together that the students found: mean + while = meanwhile.

Math Vocabulary

- Ask students to look through the poem and underline all the number words.

- Allow students to each choose one number word and use the Vocabulary 1 organizer to define the number word they chose.

Math Comprehension

- Ask the students to raise their hand and tell you how long we have to wait on the phone. (Sample answers: 17 minutes, 23 minutes, 42 minutes, 53 minutes)

- Ask the students to add the minutes we have to wait. Start with 17 + 23 = 40, then 40 + 42...

Your Call Is Very Important To Us

by Dan Greenberg

Your call is very important to us
Please remain on the line
An operator will be here to help
In approximately... *17 minutes*... time

Meanwhile please select
From the following menu choices
Dial five if you can speak into your phone
But you can't understand any voices.

Dial three if the sound is too loud or soft
Four if people sound funny
Dial star sixty-five if you'd like to pay your bill
But you just don't have any money.

To speak to a representative dial 44
Or please remain on the line
Our operators should be back from lunch
In approximately... *23 minutes*... time.

To help things flow more smoothly
Please enter the date of birth
Of your cat, your goldfish, your cousin's pet hamster
And how much your car is worth

Dial 45 if your phone went through the wash
Forty-six if run over by a truck.
Fifty seven if your phone makes rattlesnake noises
Fifty-nine if it quacks like a duck.

We value you as a customer
Your trust is something we earn
Our operators? They're off shoe-shopping now
In approximately... *42 minutes*... they'll return.

Dial 60 if you misplaced your phone
On vacation at the beach or the forest
Dial star-61 if your phone's broken or lost
Or got swallowed by a friendly stegosaurus.

We honor you as a customer
Your needs are our job Number One
Our operators are on coffee break now
In approximately... *53 minutes*... they'll be done.

If nothing else works, dial star-35
To get your free software installed
Then slowly count by ones to 999
And hopefully... you'll forget...
Why you called!

Reading in Math

Read aloud the poem, *The Elevator*, to students, modeling fluent, proficient oral reading.

- Review the long /a/ sound with students.

- Ask them to circle words that have the long /a/ sound and to notice the word endings.

- Write –ay, –ate, and –ake endings on chart paper. Ask the students to name the words from the poem that have these endings. Then write other words that have the same word endings as these words from the poem.

Math Vocabulary

- Find the vocabulary in the poem that shows putting together or taking away: addition, plus, subtraction, minus, add, subtract.

- Ask students to use Vocabulary 1 graphic organizer to define one of the words from the poem meaning putting together or taking away.

Math Comprehension

- Explain that we can check our addition problems by subtracting, and check our subtraction problems by adding. Addition and subtraction are opposites.

- In the third stanza the narrator said he pushed 12 and 17 to get 29. Check this by subtracting his answers. We will take seventeen away from twenty-nine to see if he added correctly. $29 - 17 = 12$. Is he correct?

- Continue to check his other calculations by using inverse operations.

The Elevator

Anonymous

It was a day like any other day
It began on the 17th floor.
I got up late
And after I ate
I saw a note on the elevator door.

It said: Elevator broke. This is no joke.
To get where you want to go:
Just add and subtract
Make sure you're exact
That's all you really need to know!

I pushed a few buttons, and all of a sudden,
The elevator started to climb
I added twelve and seventeen
And quickly the machine
Lifted me to the floor twenty-nine!

"Interesting," I cried, so from there I tried
Pushing 18 plus 32
The car started to rise
And to my surprise
I had a magnificent 50th-floor view.

As a change in action, I tried subtraction
Thrity-eight minus twenty-seven
A few seconds later
This subtracting elevator
Left me off at floor number eleven!

So far, I thought, this elevator has brought
Me only to floors 50 and below
But what if I tried
To go for a ride
Beyond where elevators go?

Just for fun, I pushed 47 and 31,
And for a moment I had to stand there and wait
But soon I was standing
On a very high landing
Looking down from floor seventy-eight!

Even stranger yet, please don't forget
A fact you just cannot ignore
Though my building's fairly tall with 62 floors in all I was standing
on the 78th floor!

I tried it again, pushing 76 and ten
Then I punched in 87 and 19.
In each case
I found myself in a place
That was higher than it could possibly be!

I looked at the clock, then I heard a knock
I was about to let out a scream
When I realized instead
I was still in my bed
Was the whole thing just a silly dream?

I thought, "This is weird," then my mom appeared,
And she asked me, "Are you okay?"
I ran out in the hall
To find a sign on the wall
That said ELEVATOR BROKEN TODAY.

I let out a groan. How could I have known
About the note on the elevator door?
Was it just a lucky guess?
I have to confess
It's something I may NEVER know for sure.

Reading in Math

Read aloud the poem, *Counting Coins*, to students, modeling fluent, proficient oral reading.

- Explain to the students that when we write what somebody says we use quotation marks.

- Write quotation marks on chart paper. Then have the students look through the poem and circle the quotation marks.

Math Vocabulary

- Review the value of coins: penny/1 cent, nickel/5 cents, dime/10 cents, quarter/ 25 cents.

- Allow students the opportunity to choose one coin on Vocabulary 1 Chart to define.

- Share the results with the class.

Math Comprehension

- In the poem, we used pennies to count to 100 in different ways. Using nickels, dimes, and quarters count to 100.

- Use graphic organizer Two-Column Chart. Write Coin on one side and 1 dollar on the other side.

- Have the students write the coins in the coin column: penny, nickel, dime, quarter. Next allow the students to work in small groups with manipulative money to find out how many of each coin it takes to equal one dollar. Penny should be known through the poem. (Answer: penny/100, nickel/20, dime/10, quarter/4)

Counting Coins

by Jack Silbert

I counted pennies, "1, 2, 3, 4" to 100, one by one.
"I know more ways to count," said Ruth. "In fact, I know a ton!"
She counted my pennies, "2, 4, 6, 8," up to 100 by 2's.
"Counting this way is great," she said. "You will never lose!"

I counted, "5, 10, 15, 20." Yes, I counted up by 5.
And at 100 pennies, I quickly did arrive.
Ruthie took back my pennies and counted them by 10-
"10, 20, 30, 40," up to 100 once again!

So count pennies by 1's, 2's, 5's, or 10's- any way you pick.
It's not hard to remember. There is no special trick!
Count them by yourself, or count them with a friend —
If you have one dollar's worth, you'll reach 100 in the end!

Let's Count Twos

Literature Support

Anonymous

Here's an idea,
Let's count by twos.
Two eyes, two ears
Two socks, two shoes.
Two hands, two feet,
Two eggs on a plate
Too many, too much
Too hard to keep straight?
Two minutes to two
Are you almost late?
Just count by twos
Two, four… six, eight.

Another idea:
Try counting by fives.
Five fingers, five toes
Five bees in a hive.
Five nickels, five pickles
Five five-dollar bills
Five days of the week
Five porcupine quills
Five puppies, five guppies
Five wishes from a genie
Five bike-riding bears
Five plates of linguini.
Five weeks before
Spring vacation arrives?
Just sit and relax.
Try counting by fives.

Reading in Math

Read aloud the poem, *Let's Count Twos*, to students, modeling fluent, proficient oral reading.

- In the poem you hear five many times. Five is spelled with a long i and a silent e. This is called the vowel-consonant-vowel pattern.

- Many words end with a long vowel followed by a consonant and a silent vowel. Circle the words that end with a vowel, consonant, vowel.

- List all the words the students find on chart paper. Underline the vowel, consonant, vowels at the end of the words.

Math Vocabulary

- Review with students that an array can be used to organize numbers.

- We see many numbers continued throughout the poem in groups of 2s, 5s, 10s, and 3s. To better understand the amount, we can place the numbers into an array.

- Define array with the class. Make an array to illustrate the organization.

Math Comprehension

- Ask students to count how many things were counted by two. (Answer: 7) Draw a picture of each pair of items.

- Have the students count the total items. (Answer: 14) Write: Seven groups of two equals 14 objects. Next write the multiplication sentence, $2 \times 7 = 14$.

- Have the students do the same for 5s, 10s, and 3s from the poem:
  1. Draw the pictures to follow the poem.
  2. Write the word sentence.
  3. Write the multiplication sentence.

Or what about…
Counting by tens?
Ten dogs, ten frogs
Ten very best friends
Ten bicycles, ten icicles
Ten pennies I found
Ten old-fashioned car horns
That all make this sound: *A-A-OOOO-O-OGAH!*
Ten fleas named Louise
On a grizzly bear's belly
Ten watercress sandwiches
With cream cheese and jelly
Ten flowers, ten hours
To catch up on sleep
If you're still awake
Try counting ten sheep!
And finally you might try…
Counting by threes
It's fun that extends from
Your nose to your knees
Three corks, three forks
Three pieces of pie
Three unhappy crybabies
Snivel and cry
Three chirps, three burps
Three bowls of cracked pottery
Three millionaire cousins
Who just won the lottery

Reading in Math

Read aloud the poem, *Fraction Land*, to students, modeling fluent, proficient oral reading.

- We see the word bright in the poem. The word ends with the –ight ending. We say the i as a long i and the gh is silent.

- Write –ight on chart paper and ask students to name other words that have the –ight ending. (Sample answers: light, sight, tight, night)

Math Vocabulary

- Review that a fraction is part of a whole.

- In the poem the author named: two-fifths, a third, some eighths. Write out the number representations for the fractions.

- Have students name other fractions. Then pass out Vocabulary 1 Chart and allow students time to define a fraction.

Math Comprehension

- Ask students to help you come up with a list of items we buy that come as part of a whole: socks (a pair), earrings, fruit, a bag of apples, a jar of nuts.

- Draw a picture of a bag of 8 apples. Write the fraction under the picture: $\frac{8}{8}$. Explain to the students that you ate 2 of the apples. Write the remaining fraction $\frac{6}{8}$.

- Allow the students to draw and write fractions from the class list.

- Share the students' work with the class.

FRACTION LAND

by Dan Greenberg

My sister Shawnda took me shopping
I was bored out of my mind
Until I saw the words *Fraction Land*
Printed on a bright green sign.

"Hi folks, my name's Doreen,"
Said the salesperson at the door
"Welcome to Fraction Land
"Your full-service fraction superstore
"We've got many fraction pieces
"Of every color and size
"Parts, wholes, and units
"Fractions shaped like pies.

"There are so many different combinations
"So many fractions to choose
"When you shop at Fraction Land
"There's really no way you can lose!"

Well, to make a long story short
Shawnda and I did a lot of shopping
We bought two-fifths, a third, some eighths,
And kept going without stopping.
Parts, wholes, and units
Fractions shaped like a pie.
And when it was all over
When we were really done
I gave Shawnda a great big hug
And said, "Now THAT kind of shopping is fun!"

Reading in Math

Read aloud the poem, *Ruler of the Forest*, to students, modeling fluent, proficient oral reading.

- Review the sound –ous.

- Have the students circle words in the poem that have the –ous sound at the end of the word. (Sample answers: enormous, ferocious)

- List other words that have the –ous sound at the end of the word. (Sample answers: luxurious, righteous, courageous, outrageous)

Math Vocabulary

- Review the place-value mat up to the thousands place.

- Use graphic organizer 4 Column-Chart. Write ones, tens, hundreds, thousands from right to left at the top of the chart. Have the students name numbers to fill in the chart.

Math Comprehension

- Ask students to consider if you judged by the weight of each animal which one was ruler of the forest, who would win.

- Have a picture of an elephant with the weight of 1,000 pounds and a picture of a lion with the weight of 375 pounds. Write a greater than, less than, or equal to sign.

- Do the same thing for the rat and the snake, 12 pounds and 24 pounds.

- Next have students compare the length of the animals to find out who the ruler of the forest would be, depending upon size.

RULER OF THE FOREST

by Dan Greenberg

Lion and Elephant stood face to face
When along came shifty-eyed Rat
"Hello, friends," said the wily rodent
"Am I interrupting your chat?"

"This isn't a chat," said Elephant
"And you're not interrupting at all.
"My friend here claims he's king of the forest
"But he's far too puny and small!"

Rat said, "I agree completely,
"Lion's too small — that's clear
"You need to be ENORMOUS to rule this forest
"Like my good friend Elephant here."

"Hold on there, friend," Lion growled,
"I'm sorry, but I must disagree,
"It's not how big you are that matters
"It's how FEROCIOUS you can be."

Now at this point along came Python
Slithering across the grassy ground
When she spoke her tongue shot in and out
And made a horrible hissing sound.

"Now wait a minute, Mister Rat," she hissed
"I don't want to start a fight,
"But it's one or the other — Elephant or Lion
"*Both* of these creatures can't be right."

"Good point, Ms. Snake," said Mister Rat,
"What you say is quite true.
"It's one or the other, it can't be both
"I completely agree with you."

"Oh no, Sir Rat," said Elephant
"You're just avoiding a decision
"You can't agree with all *three* of us
"You must take a single position."

"Uh," said the Rat, "you're quite correct
"A position is what I must take.
"And I'll do that in just one moment,
"But right now I need a short break."

"A BREAK!" they cried, and started arguing
Stomping, roaring, and hissing
The three were so busy quarreling
They didn't notice the rodent was missing!

"Come back!" they all shouted frantically
Calling this way and that
"You need to make your decision, good friend
"Where did you go, Sir Rat?"

Now Rat was small, but he was no fool,
He saw his position as clear
It's best to agree with ALL who are bigger
Then as fast as you can — *disappear!*

Solid Shapes

Reading in Math

Read aloud the poem, *Solid Shapes*, to students, modeling fluent, proficient oral reading.

- Review the –ound sound.

- Have students circle words in the poem that have the –ound ending.

- List the words from the poem and others the students can name: around, ground, round, sound, bound.

Math Vocabulary

- Have the students recognize and name the geometry words from the poem. List all the geometry words from the poem.

- Allow students to work in small groups to define one of the words.

- Come together as a class and share the results.

Math Comprehension

- Go on a geometry search throughout the classroom or school building. Look for shapes, angles, and lines.

- Discuss all the shapes we see in our everyday lives.

- Have students create a collage of real geometry figures, by cutting pictures from magazines. Next to each shape or figure have the students label the pictures.

by Diana Griffey

Solid shapes are all around
In the sky and on the ground
The full moon is a sphere indeed
Guided by its light at night, we see.

Faces, edges, vertices
Show how different each shape can be
Look at a cube or through a cylinder
Different faces come through clear

Pyramids, so many faces we see
Triangle sides—one, two, three.
Prism shows us your true name
Faces of rectangles not all the same

Solid shapes look and see
Here and there for all to see.

Time Passes

by Ilo Orleans

Sixty seconds
Pass in a minute…
Sixty minutes
Pass in an hour.
Twenty-four hours
Pass in a day-
And that's how TIME
Keeps passing away!

Reading in Math

Read aloud the poem, *Time Passes*, to students, modeling fluent, proficient oral reading.

- Explain to students that when we talk or write about more than one thing we add an –s or –es to the word. Adding an –s or –es to a word makes that word plural, meaning more than one.

- Have the students circle words that are plural throughout the poem. (Sample answers: seconds, minutes, hours, passes)

Math Vocabulary

- Pass out organizer Vocabulary 1. Allow students to define time in the best way they can, on the organizer.

- Have students share their definitions. Explain that time can be measured in different ways and that it depends on the length of time to decide the best way to measure it (e.g., You would not want to measure a day in seconds because the number would be too large to remember).

Math Comprehension

- Use a sequencing chart graphic organizer to organize the information from the poem. Each box in the chart should have a conversion: 60 seconds = 1 minute, 60 minutes = 1 hour, etc. Help the students add information to tell how many days in a week and how many weeks in a year.

Reading in Math

Read aloud the poem, *Super Sam vs. Two-Digit Addition*, to students, modeling fluent, proficient oral reading.

- Review rhyming words. Have students look through the poem for rhyming words. Then have them circle the words that rhyme.

- Discuss that rhyming words do not have to have the same ending spelling but rather, the same ending sound.

- After they are finished ask if they see a pattern with the rhyming words.

Math Vocabulary

- We can add three-digit numbers the same way Super Sam added two-digit numbers. We just need to line up the numbers.

- Review the ones, tens, and hundreds place value by using the Vocabulary 1 chart.

Math Comprehension

- Use the Three-Column Chart to organize adding. Put ones, tens, and hundreds in the top of the chart then have the students line up their problems.

- Call out three-digit numbers, for the students to add together, with the help of their chart.

SUPER SAM VS. TWO-DIGIT ADDITION

by Dan Greenberg

My name is Super Sam.
I'm super. I'm cool. I'm tough.
When it comes to solving Math problems
I just can't ever seem to get enough!

But wait, what's this? Good grief!
Is this one of those sneaky-snake tricks?
How do you expect me to add TWO-digit numbers
Like forty-one plus twenty-six?

The truth is I'm pretty clever
With numbers I've always been strong
But when I try doing these two-digit problems
My answers keep coming out WRONG!

Now I'm in a super tizzy
I'm super confused and perplexed.
I know my first step is to write down both numbers
I just don't know what to do next.

I stare out the window at the playground
At kids lining up by the door
Hold on! Whoah! Is this what I need?
The clue I've been searching for?

I look at flowers in the garden
All lined up in neat little rows
Are numbers a bit like tulips?
They are in some ways, I suppose.

If you arrange your numbers like flowers
Or like playground kids in straight lines
It's suddenly easy to add up the digits
To get answers that turn out just fine!

For example, to begin a problem
Like thirty-seven plus forty-one
Line up the one under the seven
You've got to admit, this is fun!

Now line up the three and the four
And remember to keep columns straight
Add the digits together and what do you get?
Thirty-seven plus forty-one is seventy-eight!

This method works on any two-digit problem
So there's nothing much more I can say
So remember when adding your two-digit numbers
Always do it the Super Sam way!

Reading in Math

Read aloud the poem, *Are We There Yet?*, to students, modeling fluent, proficient oral reading.

- Review with students that the –ed ending means past tense or that it already happened.

- Send the students to look for –ed endings throughout the poem (possible answers: finished, counted, started, guessed).

Math Vocabulary

- Use Vocabulary 1 Chart to define three-digit subtraction.

- Ask the students to help identify examples and non-examples.

Math Comprehension

- Ask the students what the narrator of the poem did while she was on the long drive to Chicago. Have the students underline: read 103 times, counted 498 cows, and saw 248 billboards.

- Have the students put the numbers in order from least to greatest.

- Next use 3-Column Chart to find out how *many more* cows than reading, $498 - 103 =$, and how many more cows than billboards, $498 - 242 =$.

Are We There Yet?

by Dan Greenberg

Two hundred and twelve miles to Chicago, Illinois.
I finished my puzzle, I've played with my toys.
I'm stuck in the back, one girl and two boys
Can you tell me, please: *Are we there yet?*

I've read my storybook 103 times
I've counted 498 cows and 242 billboard signs
We've been driving since a quarter to nine…
And all I want to know is: *Are we there yet?*

It seems we started out *years* ago
Why does the time seem to move so slow?
Are we getting any closer? I just don't know.
Can somebody tell me: *Are we there yet?*

I'm hungry, I'm tired, I should be in bed
I'm stuck in this car with my brothers instead.
Please, can we pull over at that rest stop ahead?
It'll help us figure out *if we're there yet.*

My legs are cramping, my feet are asleep
My mouth is so dry I can barely speak
My MP3 batteries are old and getting weak
So here's my question: *Are we there yet?*

My brothers keep wrestling and spilling their juice
Anthony burps and then blames it on Bruce
Is it possible that Bob, their pet lizard got loose?
And that's why I want to know if we're *there yet.*

Out the window I spy a mileage sign
It's now one twenty three to the Illinois line.
Can it possibly be — I feel like crying!
Can somebody explain why we're not *there yet?*

Here's something new, a big blue lake
Water so sparkly it makes your eyes ache
I'm so tired and bored, I can't stay awake
So tell me please: *Are we there yet?*

Out the window grey clouds and a shower
I must've been sleeping for over an hour
Hey what's that I see, a skyscraper tower?
Is it possible *we could be there yet?*

No longer tired, grumpy, or blue
There is just one question I have for you
Is that Chicago, Illinois that's come into view?
In other words: *Are we there yet?*

I've got one final question, as you might've guessed
Without for delay, I'll get it off my chest:
Are we there yet? What? The answer is YES!
Oh I'm so glad that we're *finally there yet!*

Lesson-by-Lesson Literature Connections

Use Place Value to 100 and Patterns (p. 13)

Lesson 1-1 (p. 17)

Out for the Count: A Counting Adventure
by Kathryn Cave

- Have students count the wolves, using picture groupings (5, 10, 12). Have students count the pythons using the tens groupings (10, 20, 23).

- Continue counting each picture, focusing on the groupings and how those groupings match the numeral (10, 20, 30, 36 goats): 3 groups of 10 and 6 left over = 36.

- Make a chart showing what was counted, how they were grouped, and the numeral. Record the number in words.

- Ask students to pick a number to illustrate in groups of tens. Have them record the numeral in words. Collect their illustrations and make a class book.

Lesson 1-2 (p. 21)

The Case of the Missing Birthday Party
by Joanne Rocklin

Materials: base 10 models, paper

- Give students base 10 models (strips and units, rods & cubes, etc.). Have students use a piece of paper labeled *tens* on the left and *ones* on the right to organize their models.

- Read the story. Pauline thinks the party is at 5 Twig Street, so have students show 5 with their models.

- Liz thinks a number is missing in the tens place. Let students suggest and model possible two digit numbers that have a 5 in the ones place.

- List the possible addresses on the board and cross out numbers as they are eliminated. Circle the party address.

Lesson 1-3 (p. 25)

The Case of the Missing Birthday Party
by Joanne Rocklin

- Play "What's the Address?" Choose a student leader to select an address less than 100. Have students try to guess it by asking yes and no questions. List the questions on a Yes/No T-chart. Possible questions: Is the address greater than 40? Is the number in the ones place less than 4?

- Continue until the address is discovered. The student who guesses correctly is the new leader.

- Variation: Have students guess an address, and have the leader respond "higher" or "lower." Tell students to refine their guesses based on the feedback. Record the guesses in a Higher/Lower T-chart. Continue until the address is discovered.

Lesson 1-4 (p. 27)

One Hundred Ways to Get 100 by Jerry Pallotta

Materials: hundreds boards, counters

- Give each student a hundreds board and some counters. Count with students by ones, twos, fives or tens, and have them place a marker on each number.

- Ask students to identify patterns on their hundreds boards.

- Write a number on the blackboard. Have students model the number using tens and ones.

Lesson 1-5 (p. 29)

The Grapes of Math: Mind Stretching Math Riddles
by Greg Tang

- Show each picture and ask students to estimate how many objects (fish, grapes, snails, etc.) are in it. Share strategies.

- Read the poem and discuss Mr. Tang's counting suggestion.

- After several examples, place the book in a center. Students can continue estimating using the visual clues.

- Read and enjoy Greg Tang's *Math for All Seasons* and continue estimating.

Lesson 1-6 (p. 33)

Henry the Fourth by Stuart J. Murphy

Materials: cards with the months of the year

- Give twelve students in the class a card that states one month of the year. Line those students up in front of the class out of order. Have the other students in the class put the months of the year in order.

- Have students in the class look at the alphabet. Call out a letter and ask students to identify the letter by its number position in the alphabet.

- Take students to the school parking lot. Have them identify which car, by color, is in which number position.

Lesson 1-7 (p. 35)

More or Less by Stuart J. Murphy

- As you read the story, stop and ask students to guess ages before Eddie does.

- **What is a number greater than 42? What is a number less than 46?** As students guess numbers, write the inequalities on the board.

- After reading, have students secretly write a number between 10 and 20. Turning to a partner, have each child guess the other number by asking questions. The child responding should indicate whether the number is greater than or less than the guess. Challenge students to guess within 3 questions.

Lesson 1-8 (p. 39)

Spunky Monkeys on Parade by Stuart J. Murphy

- Line up 10 students in twos. Have the first pair take a step forward as the "audience" calls out *two*, and have the second pair move forward as they call out *four*. Continue to 10, then have the two groups switch.

- Explain that you are a wheel salesman and you have to figure out how many wheels you can sell. The first 10 vehicles have one wheel. Sketch 10 unicycles on the board. The second 10 vehicles have two wheels (bicycle). Continue with 3 wheels (tricycle) and 4 wheels (car). Show how to use skip counting to find totals.

Lesson 1-10 (p. 43)

One Hundred Hungry Ants by Elinor J. Pinczes

- Read and discuss the story. Discuss other living things that come in hundreds (leaves, grass, etc.)

- Have each student gather two blades of grass. Use a Hundred Chart to count the blades by twos.

- Repeat the activity with 3, 4, and 5 blades of grass.

CHAPTER 2 Apply Addition Concepts (p. 51)

Lesson 2-1 (p. 55)

The Grapes of Math by Greg Tang

Materials: board magnets

- Before reading, emphasize that this book has some "tricks" to make mental math easy, so the class needs to pay close attention. Focus on grade appropriate examples, such as counting by tens and fives.

- After the story, use board magnets to make five groups of ten. Split the groups into twos and eights. Demonstrate counting by ones, then by twos and eights, and finally by "looking for tens."

- Repeat the example with different combinations (e.g., threes and sevens) to show how "looking for tens" is more efficient.

- Distribute connecting cubes to small groups and have them demonstrate their own examples.

Lesson 2-2 (p. 57)

100th Day Worries by Margery Cuyler

Materials: number lines, connecting cubes

- Give students 1–100 number lines. As you read the story, have them track the addition of each set of objects using the number line.

- Hand out 100 cubes. Reread the items that Jessica collects and have students place the appropriate number of cubes in piles along a line. Demonstrate "counting on" by pointing to each pile of cubes as the students "count on" each subtotal.

- Have students suggest different objects in the classroom (e.g., 8 charts, 5 pencils). Write these on the board until students think there are 100. Use "counting on" to determine the total.

Lesson 2-3 (p. 61)

The Berenstain Bears and the Missing Dinosaur Bone by Stan and Jan Berenstain

Materials: number cubes

- Read the story, focusing on solving for the unknown.

- Have pairs of students roll number cubes to get two numbers. Challenge them to use these numbers to create a math sentence with one addend and the sum, leaving the second addend a mystery. (e.g., with 8 and 2, a sentence might be 2 + ▨ = 8.)

- Have pairs use one of their mystery sentences to create a word problem about the story. For example, Snuff buried one bone. He had three this morning. How many did he eat? 1 + 2 = 3. Trade and solve by writing the math sentence to match the words.

Lesson 2-4 (p. 63)

Double the Ducks by Stuart J. Murphy

- Read the first half of the story. Record the number of children, hands, food sacks, bundles of hay, and ducks. Stop reading when the ducks bring back a friend.

- Predict how many ducks there will be now. **How much hay, food, hands, and children will now be needed?**

- Check the predictions by finishing the story.

- **If there had been 6 children, 7 tools, 8 sacks of food, 9 bales of hay, and 10 turkeys, how much would there be if these all doubled?**

- Encourage students to write their own doubling story.

Lesson 2-5 (p. 67)

Double the Ducks by Stuart J. Murphy

Materials: grid paper, crayons

- Give each student a sheet of $\frac{1}{2}$-inch grid paper.

- Have students use crayons to color 2 rows of 8 squares each to show the double 8 + 8. Have them record the addition sentence below their coloring. Then have students repeat this procedure, coloring another square in a different color to show 8 + 9.

- Ask students how they can find out the sum of 8 + 9 if they know the sum of the double is 8 + 8 (by adding one more to 16 to get 17). Have students write this addition sentence.

Note: There is another book that can be used: *Two of Everything* by Lily Toy Hong.

Lesson 2-6 (p. 71)

How Much Is That Guinea Pig in the Window? by Joanne Rocklin

Materials: connecting cubes

- Examine the pet prices. Find the tens and ones in each price. Add the cost of the Guinea Pig and the cage, focusing on 5 + 5 making 10.

- Add the tally marks, making groups of tens.

- Add the soda cans and Brad's and Jon's cans to the total. Make tens. **Can you do it mentally?**

- Have pairs of students roll dice to generate sample numbers of cans for the next 5, 10, 14 days. Add the totals.

Lesson 2-7 (p. 73)

Mall Mania by Stuart J. Murphy

- Stop reading after Heather gathers each report and ask students to find the sum. Share strategies and discuss the strategies of the book's characters.

- Heather uses the calculator. Encourage students to find the ongoing totals mentally, using models, and/or with paper (share strategies). Verify their results.

- Extension: Divide the class into four groups (one for each entrance). Reread the book and have each group keep track of their entrance's totals. **Which entrance had the most? The least?**

- Find the grand total of the 4 entrances. **Does it match the previous total?**

CHAPTER 3 Apply Subtraction Concepts (p. 83)

Lesson 3-1 (p. 87)

Ten Sly Piranhas by William Wise

Materials: rulers

- Give students rulers to use as number lines.

- Have the students put their fingers on the 10 on their ruler to represent the number of piranhas. As you read the story, have students count backward and move their finger to show how many piranhas are left.

- Retell the story, but change the number being eaten (2, 3, 2, 2, 1). Have students count backward and move their marker.

- Extension: Change the number line to 0–100 in multiples of 10. Piranhas disappear in groups of ones or tens (2, 20, 31, etc.).

Lesson 3-2 (p. 89)

Hershey's Kisses Subtraction Book by Jerry Pallotta

Materials: cubes or counters

- Share the story. Have students model the subtraction with cubes or counters

- Reread the first part of the story, but change it to subtracting all: 3 pictures − 3 pictures = 0, 10 − 10 = 0, etc. Discuss what happens when a number is subtracted from itself.

- Reread the first part again and change it to subtracting none: 3 pictures − 0 = 3 pictures, 10 − 0 = 10, etc. Discuss what happens when zero is subtracted from a number.

Lesson 3-3 (p. 91)

Domino Addition by Lynette Long, Ph.D.

Materials: dominoes

- Use a set of double 9 dominoes. Select all the doubles. (Overhead dominoes would be useful.)

- Have students sketch each double domino and write an addition problem below the sketch.

- Start with the total dots and cover one end. **How many dots are left?** Sketch, shading the covered end and record the corresponding subtraction problem (12 − 6 = 6). Sketch and record each double subtraction problem.

- Extension: What dominoes have halves that differ by 1? Sketch and write an addition and subtraction problem for each one (8 + 9 = 17, 17 − 8 = 9, and 17 − 9 = 8).

Lesson 3-4 (p. 93)

Subtraction Action by Loreen Leedy

- Read *What is the Difference* to review key vocabulary concept. Solve the problem.

- After reading *Minus Magic* review the concept. Solicit student suggestions to solve the problem. **What number pattern (operation) was used to find the answer?** Write the number sentence.

Lesson 3-5 (p. 97)

Sea Sums by Joy N. Hulme

Materials: counters

- Read the story and have students model the addition and/or subtraction with counters.

- Have students model the inverse. Example: 3 crabs + 2 crabs = 5 crabs. Inverse: 5 crabs − 3 crabs = 2 crabs.

- Examine the equations that involve imbedded inverse operations: the lionfish $1 + 2 − 1 = 2$ $[2 + (1 − 1)] = 2$; the booby $6 + (2 − 2) = 6$.

- Discuss inverse operations and how students see the connection between addition and subtraction.

Lesson 3-6 (p. 101)

Safari Park by Stuart J. Murphy

Materials: counters

- Hand out counters to students. Read the story.

- Chad shared his plan for his tickets. Before turning the page, have students determine how many monkey games he can play. Ask students to share how they found their answers. Verify with the book. Repeat the process to find Alicia's Jungle King rides.

- Patricia's plan is over her 20-ticket limit. Have students suggest ways to get her total to 20. Repeat, finding the missing addend for Abby's tickets.

- Find how many tickets Paul won. The Tarantula Ride takes 6 tickets. **How many people (including Paul) can ride on it? How do you know?**

Lesson 3-7 (p. 103)

Math Fables by Greg Tang

Materials: colored cubes

- Read the poems for 1, 2, 3, and 4.

- Using four cubes (one blue and three red), model and write math sentences to match the 4 poem. 4 squirrels − 3 frightened = 1 left to suggest a plan: $4 − 3 = 1$. Write or tell stories for $4 − 1 = 3$, $3 + 1 = 4$, and $1 + 3 = 4$

- Have students explain their number sentences and write them numerically.

- Record fact families for $2 + 2 = 4$ and $4 + 0 = 4$. Repeat, finding fact families for sums $1 − 10$ (may take several days).

- Post the fact families in the classroom.

4 Organize and Use Data (p. 113)

Lesson 4-1 (p. 117)

Bart's Amazing Charts by Diane Ochiltree

- Read the story. Discuss tally marks and how to read them. Bart's sports cards were divided into 3 categories. Ask students how many sports cards were in each group.

- Convert the picture graph of Jessica's and Bart's baskets into a tally chart.

- The sandwich survey was done with check marks. Redo it using tally marks. Discuss the ease of counting tally marks versus check marks.

- Extension: Take your own survey, recording your results with tally marks; make a graph of the results.

Lesson 4-2 (p. 119)

10 For Dinner by Jo Ellen Bogart

- Divide students into 2 groups, a hats group and a clocks group, and have them draw pictures. Have the hat group draw 2 firefighter, 1 surgeon, 1 pirate, 2 cowboy, 3 clown, and 1 Loch Ness Monster hats. Have the clocks group use clock stamps to make five 5:00 pictures, two 5:10, two 5:15, and one 3:45.

- As you read the story, show the arrival clocks in a picture graph.

- Show the hat selection in a picture graph.

- Extension: Build picture graphs of other events in the story.

Lesson 4-3 (p. 121)

The Great Graph Contest by Loreen Leedy

- Examine Gonk's graph about mud on page 5. Rewrite the graph using muddy print = 2 people instead of the one per print shown. Include a key in the new graph.

- Discuss what the pictures in the Venn diagram show on page 6.

- Make a graph of rough rocks, use a scale of one rock on the graph = 3 responses.

- Make a graph showing reptiles and birds hatching. Select a key for your graph.

Lesson 4-4 (p. 123)

Tiger Math: Learning to Graph from a Baby Tiger by Ann Whitehead Nagda and Cindy Bickel

Teacher note: The odd-numbered pages tell TJ's story. The even-numbered pages tell it in graphs.

- Compare the picture graph (p. 8) and the pie graph (p. 10). Discuss why the South China Tiger did not show up on the picture graph.

- Compare the picture graph, bar graph, and line graph of TJ's weight (pp. 12, 14, & 18).

- Do students prefer a bar graph or a line graph (pp. 16, 20) to compare TJ's and Matthew's weights?

- Extension: Discuss the data shown in the graphs about how TJ grew. Discuss rescuing animals.

Lesson 4-5 (p. 127)

Lemonade for Sale by Stuart J. Murphy

- Examine the graph on page 7; determine how many days the characters plan to sell lemonade and the maximum number cups they think they might sell.

- Compare Tuesday's results with Monday's totals. Discuss how to show 56 on this bar graph.

- Friday's total went "over the top." Ask students what they think Friday's total was, and why?

- Extension: Discuss factors that could bring lemonade sales up or down.

Lesson 4-6 (p. 129)

Lemonade for Sale by Stuart J. Murphy

- Create a bar graph for display in the classroom. Ask students how much lemonade they could drink. For example, label the x-axis: cups * 2 4 6 8 10 * (Each student marks with an X.)

- Create a "Favorite Beverage" floor bar graph.

- Create bar graph template from shower curtain. Gather data. Ask students how this activity relates to the story.

- Create a class bar graph using sticky notes. Ask students how many cups each would need for each member of their family.

Lesson 4-7 (p. 133)

Each Orange Had 8 Slices by Paul Giganti, Jr.

- Ask students the likelihood of each event. For example, if on the way to the playground you see 3 red flowers, is it likely that you saw any yellow flowers?

Model Two-Digit Addition (p. 143)

Lesson 5-1 (p. 147)

10 for Dinner by Jo Ellen Bogart

Materials: connecting cubes

- Give each student 10 connecting cubes. Read the story.

- Ask students to make different combinations that add up to 10 using the cubes. Have them write their combinations into equations.

Lesson 5-2 (p. 149)

Reese Pieces: Count by Tens by Jerry Pallotta

Materials: hundreds boards, counters

- Give each student a hundreds board and some counters. Have students start on one number and then mentally add 10 more. Have them place a counter on that number.

- Do the same activity, but have students subtract 10 from a given number.

Lesson 5-3 (p. 151)

Round Trip by Ann Jonas

Materials: mirror, number strips

- Read the story, flip the book, and complete. Establish the idea of mirror images or *opposites*.

- Demonstrate the concept by having students look into a mirror while holding up a number strip (18 becomes 81).

- Using number strips as a reference, demonstrate the concept using several combinations of numbers ($1 + 3 = 4, 4 - 3 = 1$).

Lesson 5-4 (p. 153)

A Fair Bear Share by Stuart J. Murphy

Materials: paper, tens models

- Have each student label a sheet of paper, *tens* on the left side and *ones* on the right. Using tens models (strips and units, rods and cubes, etc.) have them model the addition of the cub's nuts showing tens and ones. Share strategies and then share the book's strategy.

- Have students continue to model, add, share their strategies, and compare to the book for blueberries and seeds.

- Add Little Cub's work to the previous totals.

- Extension: **How many nuts, blueberries, and seeds did they collect altogether?**

Lesson 5-5 (p. 157)

One Duck Stuck by Phyllis Root

- After reading about the fish and the moose trying to help Stuck Duck, ask students how many total animals have tried to help so far.

- Ask the same question after the frogs try to help, and again after the snails and the snakes.

- Share strategies for adding a one-digit number to a two-digit number.

- At the end of the story, how many animals did it take to unstuck the duck in the muck?

- Extend the story by having more animals try after the dragonflies (11 mosquitoes, 12 gnats, etc.).

Lesson 5-6 (p. 159)

Sea Sums by Joy N. Hulme

- Have pairs of students represent 25 with counters on a place-value mat with tens and ones.

- Have each student take turns rolling a die and subtracting the number from 25, and trading when necessary. The first person to get to 0 or close to 0 is the winner.

- Afterward, have students repeat the game, this time starting with nothing on the board and adding to 25, trading when necessary. The first person that gets to 25 or close to it is the winner. Continue as time allows, subtracting like in the first round.

Lesson 5-7 (p. 163)

Coyotes All Around by Stuart J. Murphy

Materials: markers, hundreds board

- Give each student markers and a hundreds board.

- As the story is read, have students locate the numbers on the hundreds board. Ask students what the number should be rounded to and what their reasoning is for that decision.

- Discuss rounded sums.

- Ask students to clear their hundreds boards and place a marker on 55. **Should it be rounded to 50 or 60?** Discuss "rounding up" fives.

Lesson 5-8 (p. 165)

A Fair Bear Share by Stuart J. Murphy

Materials: paper, tens models

- Give each student a sheet of paper divided and labeled *tens* on the left and *ones* on the right, and tens models (strips & units, rods & cubes, etc.).

- Reread the story. If desired, let students suggest different numbers for each cub. For instance: first cub had 13 nuts, second cub 17 nuts, third cub 16 nuts, and fourth cub 0 nuts.

- Have students again model the addition and share strategies.

- Encourage students to try new strategies—especially ones others find efficient.

CHAPTER 6 Model Two-Digit Subtraction (p. 175)

Lesson 6-1 (p. 179)

Panda Math: Learning About Subtraction from Hua Mei and Mei Sheng by Ann Whitehead Nagda

- The left-hand pages discuss the subtraction present.

- Students find the bamboo species at the zoo and animal park that are not eaten by pandas. Examine the subtraction on page 10, and discuss the subtraction of the tens and ones.

- Find the bamboo eaten by the Bai Yun. Discuss the regrouping and the tens and one on page 14.

- In the life span problem, discuss subtracting the tens and then the ones (p. 16).

- Extend the concept by encouraging students to use "friendly tens" in their subtraction and addition work. Ask them to share their strategies.

Lesson 6-2 (p. 181)

Subtraction Action by Loreen Leedy

- Read the first 24 pages of the book. Have students quickly do the subtracting ones math.

- Have students use base-ten models and/or coins (dimes and nickels) to model Tally's and Otto's sales. After reading p. 25, do not share the pictures or read the new price. Instead, ask students to find the new price.

- Have students share strategies. Ask those who did the math mentally to share their thinking.

- After reading the rest of the book, give students rapid mental problems requiring subtracting tens ($40 - 10 = \blacksquare$, $76 - 20 = \blacksquare$, etc.), or subtract ones problems ($46 - 2 = \blacksquare$, $77 - 5 = \blacksquare$, etc.).

Lesson 6-3 (p. 183)

Elevator Magic by Stuart J. Murphy

Materials: number lines

- Read the book, noting that the elevator buttons are a vertical number line.

- On the board show a vertical number line marked in intervals of 10, from 0 to 100.

- Reread the story as a 100-floor skyscraper. Change the floors being visited. Give students a number line (vertical or horizontal) marked in intervals of 10 and allow students to retell the story with their own numbers.

Lesson 6-4 (p. 185)

Domino Addition by Lynette Long, Ph.D.

- After reading the book, explain that the class is going to write *Domino Subtraction Stories*.

- Have each student draw one domino from a pile, count and record the dots, and then use the two numbers to create a subtraction sentence.

- Increase the difficulty by having each student draw two dominoes, total the dots of each one, "and then create a subtraction problem using the larger numbers.

- Ask students to share their "stories" by drawing a picture of the dominoes used, putting their math sentence(s) below. Collect, create a cover, and "publish" the class book.

Lesson 6-5 (p. 189)

Monster Musical Chairs by Stuart J. Murphy

Materials: 0–9 spinners, paper, pencils

- Divide students up into pairs, and give each pair a 0–9 spinner, paper, and pencil.

- Have students title their papers with the number 99.

- Have each student spin the spinner and subtract the number from 99 on their paper. Have them continue subtracting until they get to zero or the lowest possible number. The student with the lowest two-digit number is the winner.

Lesson 6-6 (p. 191)

Panda Math: Learning About Subtraction by Ann Whitehead Nagda

- Have students read each subtraction word problem.

- Solve each problem.

- Have students discuss how they solved each problem.

Lesson 6-7 (p. 195)

Alexander Who Used to be Rich Last Sunday by Judith Viorst

- As you share Alexander's spending, students subtract what he spends.

- After visiting Pearson's Store, students find how much money Alexander has left.

- Ask students to check their subtraction by adding the 15¢ to their answer. Is the sum $1?

- Have students continue to keep track of Alexander's money. Ask them to check with addition.

- Extend this activity by having students find how much more money Anthony has than Nick. Check the result with addition.

Lesson 6-9 (p. 199)

Alexander Who Used to be Rich Last Sunday
by Judith Viorst

- As you revisit and reread this book, ask students to estimate how much money Alexander has left. Ask the students to share their estimation strategies.

- **About how much money does Nick have after visiting Pearson's Drug Store and betting his brothers?**

- **About how much does he have after renting the snake?**

- Continue asking for estimates after Alexander's spending events.

CHAPTER 7 Determine the Value of Money (p. 207)

Lesson 7-1 (p. 211)

Jelly Beans For Sale by Bruce McMillan

Materials: real, paper, or plastic coins

- Have students count the coins' values on each page.

- Give students coins (real, paper, or plastic) and have them show how to buy 6, 7, 8 and 9 jellybeans. Ask them to suggest more ways to make 25¢.

- Have students show how to make 11¢–24¢ to buy the corresponding number of jellybeans.

- Extension: Have students select a number of jellybeans to buy. Ask them to illustrate the page, determine which coins equaling that amount they will show, and write the text for the page. Combine these pages into a class book.

Lesson 7-2 (p. 215)

26 Letters and 99 cents by Tana Hoban

Materials: real, paper, or plastic coins

- Before reading the book, have students use coins to show 25¢. Read the book through 25¢ and discuss ways to make 25¢.

- Ask students to show 50¢, then read the book through 50¢. Then share ways to make 50¢.

- Introduce the half-dollar. Have students share alternate ways to make values shown in the book.

Lesson 7-3 (p. 217)

The Penny Pot by Stuart J. Murphy

- Read the book, but do not show the pictures and coins until students calculate how much money each person has.

- Ask students how much money Jessie has and how much more she needs. **How much money did Miguel have? How much money is in the penny pot now?**

- Repeat the above questions for Sam, Jonathan, and Annie. Discuss the counting strategies shown in the pictures.

- Extension: As a class, make a chart showing all the possible ways to make 50¢ with pennies, nickels, dimes, and/or quarters. Explore making a systematic list.

Lesson 7-4 (p. 219)

Subtraction Action by Loreen Leedy

Materials: dollars, coins

- Give each student a dollar and several of each type of coin. Read "Going, Going, Gone," and solve the word problem.

- Use the chapter pictures as reference. As amounts of money are shown in decimal notation, have students simulate the problems. For example, on p. 25, $1.00 - .25 = .75$ is pictured. Have students model with coins, "a dollar minus a quarter equals 75¢". Stress that there are several coin combinations that equal this amount. **Which combination uses the least coins?**

- Challenge the students to create their own "sale" sign and to place the appropriate money beside the number problem.

Lesson 7-5 (p. 223)

The Mon\$ter Money Book by Loreen Leedy

- Read up to the treasurer's report, then stop and ask students how many pennies make a dollar, how many dimes in a dollar, how many quarters in a dollar, and how many nickels in a dollar.

- Continue with the treasurer's report, verifying their answers to the above questions.

- **How much money does the club have in coins? in bills? altogether?**

- Extension: Discuss a budget. Can students spend, save, and give with their money?

Lesson 7-6 (p. 229)

You Can't Buy a Dinosaur with a Dime
by Harriet Ziefert

- Put a sticky-note over the oval showing Pete's total and ask students to count the money.

- Help students find how much Pete has after buying the dinosaur. Ask them how much money Pete has after cleaning the yard.

- **How much is his allowance? What is his new total?** Find the total after Pete found money and sold some baseball cards, then determine the total after Pete brought his second dinosaur.

- Extension: Discuss how students earn and spend money.

Lesson 7-7 (p. 231)

Alexander Who Used to be Rich Last Sunday
by Judith Viorst

- Give students several coins and bills, totaling one dollar, that they can use to keep track of Alexander's money as the book is read.

- Each time Alexander "spends' his money, have students subtract that amount on paper and/or with coins. $1.00 − $0.15 gum = $0.85 left.

- **After the garage sale, how much money does Alexander have?** Discuss strategies for how students subtracted Alexander's expenses.

- To extend the lesson, have students write a letter to Alexander giving him advice about how to save money.

CHAPTER 8 Measure Time and Temperature (p. 241)

Lesson 8-1 (p. 245)

Science Tools by J.A. Randolph

- Read and discuss the book. Have students focus their attention to the thermometer.

- Make a class list of why we need to know the temperature of something. (cooking food, weather and what to wear, etc.)

- Have students tell what they would wear on their birthday, based on the temperature, and why they chose what they did. If time permits, let them draw a picture of themselves on their birthday.

Lesson 8-2 (p. 249)

Go Fly A Kite! by John Burstein

- Read the story with your class. Use the discussion questions to help the students relate this event to their own lives.

- Discuss estimating how long it takes to do certain tasks. Following the discussion, have a set of pre-made cards with a set of tasks, one per card, ready to use.

- Let students draw a card, estimate how long the task will take and then let the child perform the task while the class times him or her.

- Ex. include, say the alphabet backwards, count to 50, walk to restroom and back, hop up and down 20 times, jump rope 10 times, write your full name 5 times, etc.

Lesson 8-3 (p. 253)

The Grouchy Ladybug by Eric Carle

* Read and discuss the book with the class.

* Re-read the book, allowing students to set a small clock to each time that appears in the story.

* Follow-up by letting students construct their own stories using the title "The Grouchy Puppy". Use the same format as the book. Make sure they include a clock showing the time of each event.

* Share the stories with classmates.

Lesson 8-4 (p. 255)

What's Next, Nina? by Sue Kassirer and Page Eastburn O'Rourke

* Read and discuss the story. Has something like this ever happened to class members? Discuss how the events are similar.

* Give students a snack bag with colored O's cereal and some string. Let the students string the cereals into a patterned necklace. They then swap with a partner, write down (or draw) the pattern on the necklace.

* Then have students write about the story and what they would have done about the necklace.

Lesson 8-5 (p. 259)

The Grouchy Ladybug by Eric Carle

* Read the story and help students identify if "five o'clock in the morning" is a.m. or p.m. Have students add a.m., p.m., or noon to each time.

* Have students find how much time is between the events in the story. (For example, praying mantis at 8:00 a.m. until the hyena at 1:00 p.m. is 5 hours).

* Explore quarter hour times: 5:00 sees the whale's mouth, 5:15 whale's flipper, 5:30 whale's fin, 5:45—"quarter to six"—whale's tail. Discuss ways people say the quarter hour times (quarter after, quarter 'til, half-past).

* Extension: Identify events in the school day that happen on the quarter hours and say these times in different ways.

Lesson 8-6 (p. 261)

Pigs On a Blanket by Amy Alexrod

* Give each student a small clock before reading the story.

* Read the story just for entertainment the first time.

* Read the story again and as a time is mentioned, give students the opportunity to set their clocks to reflect that time.

* Give students a sheet of paper and let them draw clocks to show the special times during the day: the time school starts, lunch, etc.

* Have them record the time of their favorite time of the day.

Lesson 8-7 (p. 265)

Science Tools by J.A. Randolph

* Read and discuss pages 6 and 7 of Science Tools. These pages discuss and introduce the thermometer.

* Be sure to have students explore the difference in Fahrenheit and Celsius.

* Have small groups of students make a list of "Things that are hot" and "Things that are cold"

* Share the list with the class.

* Discuss which things could be on either list.

* Are there things on the list that would change their appearance if they were on the other list. (ex. icewater)

9 Model Fractions (p. 279)

Lesson 9-1 (p. 283)

Gator Pie by Louise Mathews

- Draw a pie on the board. Ask a volunteer to divide it for 2 gators and record the fraction name for each part. Draw another pie and ask a volunteer to divide and label it for 3 gators.

- Repeat the process for 4 and for 8 gators. Discuss how many pieces Alice and Al ate. **What part of the pie was this?**

- Extension: Ask volunteers to divide a pie into sixths, tenths, twelfths, etc.

Lesson 9-2 (p. 285)

The Hershey's Milk Chocolate Fractions Book by Jerry Pallotta

Materials: paper chocolate bars

- Give students paper chocolate bars to model problems. Discuss how the stack of 12 small pieces equals 1 whole candy bar (rearrange back into a bar). **How do the $\frac{1}{12}$ and $\frac{11}{12}$ pictures go together?**

- Talk with students about how the $\frac{1}{2}$ bar and $\frac{6}{12}$ bar are related. Discuss, compare, and model $\frac{1}{3}, \frac{2}{3}, \frac{4}{12}$, and $\frac{8}{12}$ bar. **How do they relate?**

- Discuss, compare, and model the other fractions shown.

- Extension: Discuss $\frac{13}{12}$.

Lesson 9-3 (p. 287)

Piece=Part=Portion by Scott Gifford

- After reading the book, divide students into ten groups. Give each group a circular piece of paper to represent a pizza and a recording sheet. Explain that this circle represents one *whole*.

- Have each group draw a number ranging from 1–10, and equally divide their pizza into that many pieces. Take out one piece and record the correct fraction to represent its relationship to the whole $(1 \text{ of } 4 = \frac{1}{4})$.

- Share group results, saving the "1" group for last. Discuss the difference.

- Ask comparison questions. Challenge students to write the fraction if 2 pieces are eaten from their pizza.

Lesson 9-4 (p. 289)

Apple Fractions by Jerry Pallotta

Materials: paper apples

- Have students use paper apples to model. Talk with them about fair vs. not-fair sharing.

- Discuss sharing the apple among 3 people, and compare the pictures of $\frac{1}{3}, \frac{2}{3}$, and $\frac{3}{3}$. Compare these to 1 whole apple. Repeat with $\frac{1}{4}, \frac{2}{4}, \frac{3}{4}, \frac{4}{4}$.

- Predict how to share an apple 5 ways. **How many fifths will make the whole?** Repeat for sixths. Discuss the divisions of the Cortland apple. **Which one shows sevenths? Why?**

- Extension: Discuss $\frac{9}{8}$ and the other fractions in the story.

Discuss what you learned about apples.

Lesson 9-5 (p. 293)

Shanna's Pizza Parlor by Jean Marzallo

- Read and discuss the story. Let children share what they think would make a good pizza topping. Make a list on a chart.

- Give children a 10" circle to make their "pizza".

- Have some students divide their pizza into halves and some into fourths.

- Let the children decorate their pizza pieces with their favorite toppings. They can do each piece differently if they would like.

- Then have them compare which pieces are bigger than the others. Ex. My half is bigger than your fourth. Two fourths from my pizza is the same as half of your pizza.

Lesson 9-6 (p. 297)

Jump Kangaroo, Jump! by Stuart J. Murphy

Materials: counters

- Give students 12 counters (chips, tiles, etc.). Then read through p. 8 and have students use counters to find $\frac{1}{2}$ of 12.

- Discuss what else, besides how many players, should be considered in a fair division of sports teams.

- Read through p. 14, and have students use counters to find $\frac{1}{3}$ of 12. Continue reading through p. 20, and have students use counters to find $\frac{1}{4}$ of 12.

- Extension: **When they did the long jump, what fraction of 12 was on each team?** Divide the class into halves, thirds, fourths, etc.

Lesson 9-7 (p. 299)

Eating Fractions by Bruce McMillan

Materials: 2 paper circles per student, scissors

- Show the pictures. Before revealing the fractions, ask questions.

- On muffin page, **What fraction of the muffin does the girl have? The boy?**

- On pizza page, **If the children eat the whole pizza, how many pieces will each child get? What fraction is this? Can anyone tell me another fraction for this?** Explain how it can be divided into 2 groups of 2.

- Pass out 2 circles to each student to make "strawberry pie." Have them cut their pies into eighths.

- **How many pieces would there be altogether? If I had 1 piece of, what fraction would I eat? 2 pieces?** Etc.

- Discuss how the pieces could be grouped in groups of 2 to make 4 groups. Show how $\frac{1}{4}$ is the same as $\frac{2}{8}$.

CHAPTER 10 Use Place Value to 1,000 (p. 309)

Lesson 10-1 (p. 313)

The King's Commissioners by Aileen Friedman

- Determine how many commissioners the First Royal Advisor counted. Discuss his counting strategy. Repeat for the Second Royal Advisor.

- Discuss how the Princess organized the commissioners. Ask students how that helped her count them. Challenge them to use the Princess' method to find the total number of commissioners.

- Use the Princess' method to sketch 68 dots, 70 sticks, 100 units, 125 shells, etc.

Lesson 10-2 (p. 315)

Out For the Count: A Counting Adventure by Kathryn Cave

- Looking at the pictures, ask students to use the groupings shown to count the objects as you read the book aloud. Have students discuss their strategies for counting the pythons.

- Discuss how students know how many pirates there are in the picture. Ask students how many different ways they can count them.

- Count the bats. Can students suggest other groupings for the bats?

- The 100 shadows are not grouped; have students discuss and/or model ways to group and count 100.

Lesson 10-3 (p. 317)

The Best Vacation Ever by Stuart J. Murphy

- Read the story, calling attention to the charts. Divide students into groups of five and give each group five pieces of paper for charts.

- Using pages 24–25 as a model, have each group create and complete a warm/cold, far/near, fun/quiet, or pet/no pet chart for their group. Then tabulate and create a results chart (p. 27).

- If time allows, combine the group data to ascertain the perfect destination for a class trip.

- To tie the idea to place value, have pairs of students draw or spin for numbers, record on a place value chart, add, and report answers.

Lesson 10-4 (p. 319)

The Case of the Missing Birthday Party
by Joanne Rocklin

- After finding the party is not at 5 Twig Street, the detective kids decide it is at "something-5". List possible addresses (15, 25, 35...). Ask students what addresses they checked first.

- Discuss which addresses are possible if there is a 5 in the hundreds place.

- Talk about how the detective kids were able to limit the search to an address less than 100. **What house numbers were left to be checked when the detective kids decided to follow the other guests?**

- Extension: Ask students if they have a 5 in their address, and what place-value position it is in.

Lesson 10-5 (p. 323)

Earth Day—Hooray by Stuart J. Murphy

- Read the story. **How do you know how many cans they collected the first day? How did Carly know there were 56 cans?**

- Discuss how they bagged the 635 cans, and how many 100 bags went into the 1000 bag.

- **How many of each sized bag made up 2852 cans? If all the bags were combined, how many of each size totaled 5026?**

- Extension: Read and discuss the large numbers on the fact signs throughout the book.

Lesson 10-7 (p. 329)

Just Enough Carrots by Stuart J. Murphy

- Have students look at the carrots, explaining that the bunny and the bird have 4 carrots each, the horse has 12 carrots, and the elephant has only 1. Rewrite these facts using $>$ $=$ $<$: bunny's $=$ bird's, horse's $>$ bunny's, elephant's $<$ bunny's.

- Compare bunny's, squirrel's, bird's, and elephant's peanuts using $>$ $<$ $=$.

- Compare bunny's, frog's, bird's, and elephant's worms using $>$ $<$ $=$.

- Extension: Write larger numbers on the board and ask students to use $>$ $<$ $=$ to compare numbers.

Lesson 10-8 (p. 331)

Less Than Zero by Stuart J. Murphy

- Draw a number line on the board from -5 to $+10$. Write the negative numbers in red. Use a magnet to show Perry's clams on the number line, starting at zero clams.

- Read the story, moving the magnet to show his clams after trimming the ice. Continue to keep track of his clams through the story.

- Discuss the lesson Perry learned.

- Extension: Make an open number line with only the hundreds marked and ask students to place numbers on it.

Lesson 10-9 (p. 333)

The 512 Ants on Sullivan Street by Carol A. Losi

- While reading the story, record the number of ants on a list.

- After the 4 ants with a chip, 2 ants with pieces of plum, and 1 ant with a crumb, ask students to predict how many ants will be next.

- As you read the story, ask students to continue to predict the next number of ants for each situation. Discuss strategies and patterns students used for making their predictions.

- Extension: This pattern shows base-two. Explore other bases; rewrite the story with ants in base-four (1, 4, 16, 64, 256...). Discuss the pattern for base-ten.

CHAPTER 11 Understand Geometric Shapes and Spatial Reasoning (p. 341)

Lesson 11-1 (p. 345)

Cubes, Cones, Cylinders, & Spheres by Tana Hoban

Materials: geometric solids

- This is a wordless book with photographs capturing the sphere, cone, cube, and cylinder. Have 3D models available for students to examine.

- Examine the blocks, ice cream cones, cylinders, and road cones. Ask students to describe the characteristics of each shape.

- Continue through the book asking students to describe shapes until there is a consensus definition of each shape.

- Introduce rectangular prisms as you look at the stacks of cubes in the foam castle.

- Extension: Look for cubes, cones, cylinders, spheres, pyramids, and rectangular prisms in the classroom.

Lesson 11-2 (p. 347)

Captain Invincible and the Space Shapes by Stuart J. Murphy

Materials: geometric solids

- Before reading the story, use geometric solids to set out the instrument panel shown on p. 7. Have students identify how the solids are organized.

- Ask a student to "push" and identify each button as it is indicated in the story. After pushing a "button", have students identify the faces named in the story.

- Ask students to identify geometric shapes in the pictures.

- Extension: Use the solids to identify vertices and edges.

Lesson 11-3 (p. 351)

Grandfather Tang's Story by Ann Tompert

Materials: construction paper shape cut outs or pattern blocks

- Read the story and discuss the different shapes throughout.

- Have students point out how the different shapes are used to create different pictures. For example, ask students, **What shapes are used to create the hawk's wings?**

- After reading, give students each of the tan shapes. Conduct a quick review of shapes by having students hold up different shapes or call out different attributes about the shape. For example, **Hold up a shape that has only 3 sides.**

- Next, allow students to create their own character the fox could have turned into.

- Students can write a sentence below their picture stating what their fox turned into and why.

Lesson 11-4 (p. 353)

Grandfather Tang's Story by Ann Tompert

Materials: traced puzzle pieces

- Duplicate or trace the puzzle pieces on the Tangrams page so that each student has a set of tans (the name for the pieces).

- Allow students to work in pairs to simulate Grandfather and Little Soo, rearranging tans as the story progresses. Use **formal** vocabulary to help students create the correct configuration of the pieces.

Lesson 11-5 (p. 357)

The Greedy Triangle by Marilyn Burns

- While reading the story, develop a chart listing the name, examples, sides, and vertices (angles) of each shape.

- Discuss places students see triangles and the sides and vertices of the triangles. Discuss places you see each shape and identify how many sides and angles each shape has.

- Ask students what relationship they notice between the number of angles (vertices) and the number of sides of polygons.

Lesson 11-6 (p. 359)

Circus Shapes by Stuart J. Murphy

- While reading the book, use the book's questions to guide discussion about plane/solid shapes and their attributes.

- Using solid shapes, have students identify the plane faces of solid figures, such as a cube, pyramid, or rectangular prism.

- Have the students identify plane faces within solid shapes in their classroom environment.

- Record students' responses on a T-chart with headings of *Plane Faces* and *Solid Shapes.*

Lesson 11-7 (p. 361)

Three Pigs, One Wolf, and Seven Magic Shapes by Grace Maccarone

- If possible, give students tangrams to use. While reading the description of the seven pieces, have students hold up the pieces.

- Build the cat on the overhead, and have students do the same at their desks.

- Have students build shapes, as time permits. Start a shape on the overhead and invite students to finish it, or allow students to make the shapes on their own.

Lesson 11-9 (p. 365)

Rock It, Sock It, Number Line by Bill Martin and Michael Sampson

- Read and discuss the book.

- Put a number line on the board where the class can see it. As you reread the story, have students locate the number on the page on the number line.

- Put a number line on the floor or outside on the sidewalk. Roll a 10-sided die and let a student hop to that number. Continue doing this until all the numbers have someone on them.

- Select a number and put a sticker on it. If the sticker is rolled, then everyone gets off the number line and you start over.

Lesson 11-10 (p. 367)

Rock It, Sock It, Number Line by Bill Martin and Michael Sampson

- Review the book.

- As you reread the story, explain to students that they will help you create a vegetable garden like the one in the book.

- Introduce coordinate graphs. Explain that these help show where things are located. Illustrate by drawing a simple coordinate graph. Show students how to navigate (always start at 0, then count to the right, then count upward.)

- Plot some vegetables on your coordinate graph. Ask students to use numbers to tell where each vegetable is located. Tell students that people's gardens are laid out this way.

 **Measure Length and Area** (p. 375)

Lesson 12-1 (p. 379)

Super Sand Castle Saturday by Stuart J. Murphy

- Read the story, focusing on pp. 1–19. **How will you know which castle is the tallest, longest, or has the deepest moat?**

- Ask students how many shovelfuls Juan's and Sarah's castles needed. If students notice the difference in shovel size, discuss this.

- Ask students if spoons are good measuring tools, and why they think the way they do.

- **How do you know whose castle was the longest?** Discuss the use of nonstandard items to measure.

Lesson 12-2 (p. 381)

Super Sand Castle Saturday by Stuart J. Murphy

Materials: masking tape

- Ask students how Larry will know which castle is the tallest, longest, or has the deepest moat.

- Use masking tape or adding machine tape to show Sarah's 44-inch tower, Juan's 48-inch tower, and Laura's 40-inch tower. Compare the heights.

- Model with tape, or draw lines on the board to show and compare the depths of the moats and the lengths of the castles.

- Extension: Compare which is longest, shortest, and how much longer or shorter than each other they are. Discuss Larry's comment, "...an inch is always an inch."

Lesson 12-3 (p. 385)

Centipede's 100 Shoes by Tony Ross

- Read and discuss the book. After you have completed the book pose the following problem to the class.

- It took Centipede's 10 aunts 10 hours to knit 50 socks for the centipede. Now only 5 of his aunts can finish the job the next day. The other five had a tea party to attend. How long will it take the 5 aunts to knit the 50 socks that Centipede still needs.

- Make a chart for the class to use in solving this problem. If 10 aunts knit 50 socks, how many did each one knit? How long did it take each aunt to knit those 5 socks?

- Now if 1 aunt took 2 hours to knit 1 sock, how long will it take 5 aunts to knit 50 socks? Each aunt will need to knit 10 socks. (20 hours)

- Discuss each step thoroughly and make sure you keep the steps small and easy to follow.

Lesson 12-4 (p. 387)

Inchworm and a Half by Elinor J. Pinczes

Materials: rulers, objects of different sizes

- Before reading the story, give each student a ruler. When a measurement is mentioned have students determine that length on their rulers.

- Give pairs of students 3 small objects. Record each item and then **estimate** the length as accurately as possible.

- Use rulers (or inchworms made from colored number strips with dots for the eyes and labeled with the amount) to check the validity of the estimates. Trade items with other pairs and repeat the process.

- Close by asking comparison questions. Ask students to verify their responses with measured objects.

Lesson 12-5 (p. 391)

Measuring Penny by Loreen Leedy

Materials: rulers

- Read the story, then measure the width of the paws shown in the book. Confirm the author's results.

- Using centimeters, have the students measure the width of their "paws" (hands). Then have them measure the width of their other "paws" (feet).

- Measure the paws, ears, height, etc. of stuffed animals in centimeters or decimeters.

Lesson 12-6 (p. 393)

Polly's Pen Pal by Stuart J. Murphy

- Have students find Montreal, Canada on a map.

- Tape cm measuring tapes to the wall or bookcases, and have students find their height by standing next to the tape.

- Sort students by height. **Which are taller, shorter, or the same as Ally?**

- Have them measure a baseball bat. **Is yours about 1 meter long?**

- Use a 1-meter trundle wheel or a metric tape to measure the length of the school hallway or gym.

Literature Support

Literature Support

Lesson 12-7 (p. 395)

Big, Better, Best by Stuart J. Murphy

- Read and discuss the book. Have students pay attention to how the windows were alike and how they were different. How did they measure them?

- Give each child 12 color tiles or one-inch cubes and have them create a shape using all twelve. Let them trace the shape on a plain piece of paper.

- Now, on a separate sheet, have them use those same twelve pieces to create a different shape. Trace the new one on a paper.

- Let the group show what variations they came up with as they created the shapes.

- Lead them to the understanding that all the shapes have the same area and how they know that.

Measure Capacity and Weight (p. 405)

Lesson 13-1 (p. 409)

A House for Birdie by Stuart J. Murphy

- Read and discuss the story with the class. Discuss the concept that different houses will hold different birds due to size and shape.

- Collect different shoes including running shoes (for children and adults), girls flats, men's dress shoes, etc.

- Fill each shoe with dried beans or centimeter cubes. Label the shoes A,B, C, etc. and let students estimate the capacity (or numbers of beans) in each. To demonstrate why nonstandard isn't accurate and consistent, use two different size beans or cubes.

- Have students explain how they arrived at their decisions. Share these discussions with the class. Allow students to revise their estimates as they proceed.

Lesson 13-2 (p. 411)

Pigs In The Pantry by Amy Axelrod

- Read and discuss the book. Talk about a time when they might have cooked for a parent or grandparent. Who helped them? What did they cook?

- Using sand, rice, or some other dry substance, let students play with measuring tools such as cups, spoons, quart and gallon containers. As they do have them decide which tools you would use to make some cookies.

- Have students write a recipe for their "famous" cookies that everyone wants. They can name them and write the recipes including directions.

Lesson 13-3 (p. 413)

How Big Is a Foot? by Rolf Myller

- Read and discuss the book. Then reread the book looking for all the characters.

- Divide the class into groups and let each group act out the story, with students assuming the roles of the main characters: the king, queen, and carpenter.

- Let each group perform for the class.

- Have students create a similar scenario and act it out.

Lesson 13-4 (p. 417)

Room for Ripley by Stuart J. Murphy

- Read and discuss the book. Be sure to discuss the pictures and what is going on.

- After reading the book, give small groups a measuring cup or container and a large container and let them estimate how many milliliters or liters it will take to fill the container. Then measure to verify students' estimates.

- Have students make a two-column chart, labeling each column with a different unit of capacity (*milliliter* or *liter*). Then have them list items they might find in each capacity (ex.,: a liter of sports drink; a milliliter of medicine)

Lesson 13-5 (p. 421)

How Heavy Is It? by Brian Sargent

- Read and discuss the book.

- Using a simple balance scale, compare the weight of an apple to 10 paper clips. What is the result? Repeat this process with two or three other small objects from your classroom.

- Now let students make a list of things in the room and things at home that weigh more than and less than an apple. Divide the class and let one group do the "more" list and the other half do the "less" list.

- Regroup and share the lists. Demonstrate a couple of them using the balance scale and the apple.

Lesson 13-6 (p. 423)

If Dogs Were Dinosaurs by David M. Schwartz

- Read and discuss the book. Give attention to the size comparisons as you read. Encourage discussions as you read.

- If you have weights, let students feel what one-pound feels like. If not, make one from a container and some sand (or rice).

- Now have a collection of objects such as an eraser, stapler, apple, pencil, book, etc on a table for students to examine.

- As a group, have them decide if an object weighs more, less, or about a pound. Put the items on a balance scale to get the answer.

Lesson 13-7 (p. 425)

Gold Fever by Verla Kay

- This story tells of the discovery of gold in 1848.

- Gold is measured/weighed in grams and a single gram of gold can be hammered into a sheet of one square meter.

- Have students use a meter stick to construct a square meter and cover the square meter with yellow paper to see the area a single gram of gold can be hammered into.

- Have students predict whether 10 grams of hammered gold would cover the floor of the classroom and then check their prediction using the meter stick and multiplication.

CHAPTER 14 Solve Three-Digit Addition and Subtraction Problems (p. 435)

Lesson 14-1 (p. 439)

Fun With Roman Numerals by David Adler

- Have students "pull apart" Roman numerals to find their values. For example, XVI = 10 + 5 + 1. Explain how VIIII = 5 + 1 + 1 + 1 + 1 leads to the "shortcut" IX.

- On p. 29 select numbers for students to find their value (do not go in order), such as XVIII and XXVII.

- P. 29 shows XXVIIII for 29; use the short cut to rewrite this.

- Extension: Create Roman numerals in the hundreds for students to find their values: CCXXXI, CLII, CCLIX, CCCXLIII, etc. Discuss the adding and subtracting of hundreds, tens, and ones.

Lesson 14-2 (p. 441)

The 329th Friend by Marjorie W. Sharmat

- Have students find sums such as: **What is the total number of eggs and tarts Emery prepared? If each bouquet had 2 flowers, how many flowers did Emery use?**

- Discuss how to find how many pieces of silverware Emery had to "set" for the tables (329 + 329 + 329).

- Tell students that each person had a dessert dish, a plate, and a glass, and ask them how many dishes that is.

- Extension: Share addition strategies. Explore non-traditional strategies.

Lesson 14-3 (p. 443)

Animal Giants by Sara Louise Kras

- Teacher Note: Similar activities can be done with any animal fact book. As you read this section, you may want to limit your reading to the paragraphs about size.

- **If a zoo loaded a Komodo dragon and an anaconda on the same truck, how much weight would that be in pounds? in kilograms?**

- **If the saltwater crocodile was added to the truck, what would the new weight be in pounds? in kilograms?**

- **Now add the leatherback turtle; what are the new totals?**

- Extension: Explore more facts about these reptiles or other animals.

Lesson 14-4 (p. 445)

Cats Add Up! by Dianne Ochiltree

- As a group, create a simple reference table of "Feline Facts," determining the numbers of ears, eyes, tails, noses, and paws per cat.

- Continue the chart to include data for 5 cats.

- As the story is read, challenge students to add and subtract tally marks to determine the final number of cats.

- Using the format of the Cat Riddles on the last page, ask students questions about the number of ears, paws, etc. Have them refer to their "Feline Facts" table to answer. Some answers should require computation (e.g. **If I count 16 paws, how many cats are in the room?**)

Lesson 14-5 (p. 447)

Coyotes All Around by Stuart J. Murphy

- Using a number line, discuss how a number is rounded.

- Discuss Clever's rounding on pp. 12 and 20.

- Check Careful's addition on pp. 13 and 21.

- Repeat this for pp. 28 and 29.

- Extension: Select activities from the author's notes at the end of the book. Practice rounding numbers—class sizes, etc. Extend to three-digit numbers.

Lesson 14-6 (p. 451)

Roman Numerals I to MM by Arthur Geisert

- Make a chart of Roman numerals and their values.

- Have students find the value of Roman numerals by adding ones, tens, and hundreds: II, XXX, CCC, etc. Have them subtract and add to show numbers IV, VIII, CXC, CCCXIX, CCVIII, etc.

- Have students use adding and subtracting to find the value of the Roman numerals (CCCXXIX, CCXXIII, etc.).

- Extension: Write dates (years) in Roman numerals.

Lesson 14-7 (p. 453)

Shark Swimathon by Stuart J. Murphy

- Have students find the total laps swam the first day and the remaining laps to be swum the rest of the week.

- Repeat the laps swam that day and the laps remaining each day.

- Share strategies for find the sums and differences as students share their thinking.

- Extension: Discuss how many laps per day they would have needed to swim if the task were done evenly over four days. **How many laps per day would that be for each shark?**

Lesson 14-8 (p. 457)

Math Mini Mysteries, "You and the Statue" by Sandra Markle

Materials: rulers

- Record the chart on the board, using cm (Nose 1.37 meters becomes 137 cm).

- Have students work in pairs to measure their mouth width (to the nearest cm). **How much wider is Miss Liberty's mouth?**

- Repeat for the length of the nose, the distance across the eyes, and the length of the index finger.

- As time allows, find the difference between the students and Miss Liberty for other measurements.

Lesson 14-9 (p. 459)

How Big Were the Dinosaurs? by Bernard Most

- Read the book and use the chart in the back to find rounded differences.

- Find an approximate size for the Seismosaurus. (about 130 ft.)

- Compare the size of other dinosaurs to the Seismosaurus; first round the length to the nearest ten and then find how much bigger the Seismosaurus is.

- Have students select dinosaurs and compare their lengths. First round the lengths and then find how much larger or smaller one dinosaur is compared to another.

- Extension: Discuss which lengths did not change when rounded. Discuss which situations require exact answers and when an approximate answer works well.

CHAPTER 15 Model Multiplication and Division (p. 469)

Lesson 15-1 (p. 473)

What Comes in 2's, 3's, and 4's? by Suzanne Aker

- Read the story to the class.

- Put up a blank chart divided into columns for 2's, 3's, 4's, and 5's.

- After reading the story let students add things to the chart. Discuss possibilities for each column.

- Let children make their own books of "What Comes In 2's, 3's, 4's?" that they can share with classmates.

- Add a second chart for 10's and 12's. Let students add ideas to the list throughout the week.

Lesson 15-2 (p. 475)

Spunky Monkeys on Parade by Stuart J. Murphy

Materials: counters

- Give students counters to model each group.

- Have students show a line of 10 pairs and count by twos. Share the picture on pp. 12–13, emphasizing that each group is the same (2). Write the equation $10 \times 2 = 20$.

- Repeat for groups of three, and groups of four. If needed, two students can combine their counters to model these.

- As a group, have them decide if an object weighs more, less, or about a pound. Put the items on a balance scale to get the answer.

Lesson 15-3 (p. 477)

Zachary Zormer, Shape Transformer by Joanne Anderson Reisberg

- Read the story.

- Tell students that they are going to write about Zachary Zormer.

- Their task is to write what happened the next Friday in class, and to share what Zachary brought in to measure.

- Review the different things that Zachary showed in class. Brainstorm a few ideas.

- Have students work in small groups.

- Students will be writing a paragraph to explain what Zachary brought to measure, and then will need to draw a picture to go along with the story.

- Instruct students that the picture should be labeled with the appropriate measurements.

Lesson 15-4 (p. 479)

Too Many Kangaroo Things to Do! by Stuart J. Murphy

Materials: connecting cubes

- Read the story, taking time to pause at the math summary pages and describe the pictures. Make note of the repeated addition examples.

- Divide the teaching board into two parts, labeling them *repeated addition* and *multiplication*. Demonstrate how to write the platypus' "2 times" multiplication sentences in both repeated addition and in multiplication. Invite students to write other examples from the "3 times" and "4 times" tables in the story.

- Distribute connecting cubes to small groups. Call out examples from the math summary pages in the story and have the students show the answers in repeated addition.

Lesson 15-5 (p. 481)

Counting Is for the Birds by Frank Mazzola Jr.

- Have three copies of the index (last page) printed out. Cut out the copies into one master set and two sections for the students. Distribute the (20) cards to students. Read the story. Use the master card set to call up students holding each type of bird (10 types). Talk about 5 groups of 2.

- Use the same cards to demonstrate different multiplication groups (two groups of red birds, $2 \times 2 = 4$; three groups of crested birds, $3 \times 2 = 6$; six groups of birds with white, $6 \times 2 = 12$). Have students think of different groups (e.g., females and males, $5 \times 2 = 10$).

Lesson 15-6 (p. 487)

Everybody Wins by Sheila Bruce

- Read and discuss the story. Draw the students' attention to the vocabulary *split*, *divide*, *each*, *three ways*, and *four ways*.

- Have them listen for number sentences. Ask them to explain what they mean.

- Give each student 20 objects such as cubes. Working in groups of 4, let them generate split up the objects into equal groups and make up a sentence explaining what they did.

Lesson 15-7 (p. 489)

One Hungry Cat by Joanne Rocklin

Materials: connecting cubes

- Ask the class if they had ever had trouble sharing evenly. Ask for a few examples of something they were trying to share.

- Draw 12 cookies on the board. Tell the students that you have to share them with one friend and ask how you should "divide" them. Write $12 \div 2 = 6$. Ask if you could share equally with 2, 3, 4, or 6 others.

- Pass out connecting cubes to groups or partners. Give some division questions, asking the students to stand if they can divide equally or sit on the floor if not.

Literature Bibliography

CHAPTER 1 Use Place Value to 100 and Patterns

Case of the Missing Birthday Party, The by Joanne Rocklin. Scholastic, Inc. 1998.

Earth Day–Hooray! by Stuart J. Murphy. HarperCollins Children's Books. 2004.

Father Who Had 10 Children, The by Benedicte Guettier. Puffin. 2001.

Grapes of Math, The by Greg Tang. Scholastic, Inc. 2001.

Henry the Fourth by Stuart J. Murphy. HarperCollins Children's Books. 1999.

One Hundred Hungry Ants by Elinor J. Pinczes. Houghton Mifflin Company. 1993.

One Hundred Ways to Get One Hundred by Jerry Pallotta. Scholastic, Inc. 2003.

Skittles Riddles Math by Barbara Barbieri McGrath. Charlesbridge Publishing, Inc. 2000.

Spunky Monkeys on Parade by Stuart J. Murphy. HarperCollins Children's Books. 2003.

CHAPTER 2 Apply Addition Concepts

100th Day Worries by Margery Cuyler. Simon & Schuster Children's Publishing. 2000.

512 Ants on Sullivan Street, The by Carol A. Losi. Scholastic, Inc. 1997.

Berenstain Bears and the Missing Dinosaur Bone, The by Stan and Jan Berenstain. Random House Books for Young Readers. 1980.

Double the Ducks by Stuart J. Murphy. HarperCollins Children's Books. 2003.

Grapes of Math, The by Greg Tang. Scholastic, Inc. 2001.

How Much Is That Guinea Pig in the Window? by Joanne Rocklin. Sagebrush Education Resources. 1995.

King's Chessboard, The by David Birch. Puffin. 1993.

Mall Mania by Stuart J. Murphy. HarperCollins Children's Books. 2006.

Ten Friends by Bruce Goldstone. Henry Holt and Co. 2001.

CHAPTER 3 Apply Subtraction Concepts

Benny's Pennies by Pat Brisson. Random House. 1993.

Domino Addition by Lynette Long. Charlesbridge Publishing, Inc. 1996.

Hershey's Kisses Subtraction Book, The by Jerry Pallotta. Scholastic, Inc. 2002.

How Many Bluebirds Flew Away? by Paul Giganti.

M&M's Counting Book, The by Barbara Barbieri McGrath. Charlesbridge Publishing, Inc. 1994.

Math Fables by Greg Tang. Scholastic, Inc. 2000.

Safari Park by Stuart J. Murphy. HarperCollins Children's Books. 2001.

Sea Sums by Joy N. Hulme. Hyperion Books for Children. 1996.

Subtraction Action by Loreen Leedy. Holiday House. 2000.

Ten Sly Piranhas by William Wise. Penguin Books USA, Inc. 1993.

CHAPTER 4 Organize and Use Data

10 for Dinner by Jo Ellen Bogart. Scholastic-TAB Publications Ltd. 1989.

Bart's Amazing Charts by Diane Ochiltree. Scholastic, Inc. 1999.

Five Creatures by Emily Jenkins. Farrar, Straus, Giroux. 2001.

How Much Is That Guinea Pig in the Window? by Joanne Rocklin. Sagebrush Education Resources. 1995.

Judge: An Untrue Tale by Harve Zemach. Farrar, Straus, Giroux. 1988.

Lemonade for Sale by Stuart J Murphy. HarperCollins Children's Books. 1998.

Mission Addition/There Was an Old Lady Who Swallowed a Fly by Loreen Leedy/Simms Taback. Holiday House. 2002.

Tiger Math: Learning to Graph from a Baby Tiger by Cindy Bickel. Henry Holt and Company, LLC. 2000.

CHAPTER **5** **Model Two-Digit Addition**

10 for Dinner by Jo Ellen Bogart. Scholastic, Inc. 1989.

Coyotes All Around by Stuart J. Murphy. HarperCollins Children's Books. 2000.

Fair Bear Share, A by Stuart J. Murphy. HarperCollins Children's Books. 1998.

M & M's Addition Book, The by Barbara Barbieri McGrath. Charlesbridge Publishing, Inc. 2004.

Mall Mania by Stuart J. Murphy. HarperCollins Children's Books. 2006.

Mission Addition by Loreen Leedy. Holiday House. 1997.

Reese's Pieces Count by Tens by Jerry Pallotta. Charlesbridge Publishing, Inc. 2000.

Round Trip by Ann Jonas. HarperCollins Children's Books. 1983.

Sea Sums by Joy N. Hulme. Hyperion Books for Children. 1996.

Tail Feather Fun: Counting by Tens by Michael Dahl. Picture Window Books. 2006.

Toasty Toes: Counting by Tens by Michael Dahl. Picture Window Books. 2006.

 CHAPTER **6** **Model Two-Digit Subtraction**

Domino Addition by Lynette Long, Ph.D. Charlesbridge Publishing, Inc. 1996.

Elevator Magic by Stuart J. Murphy. HarperCollins Children's Books. 1997.

M & M's Subtraction Book, The by Barbara Barbieri McGrath. Charlesbridge Publishing, Inc. 2005.

Math for All Seasons by Gregory Tang. Scholastic Press. 2002.

Monster Musical Chairs by Stuart J. Murphy. HarperCollins Children's Books. 1989.

More M & M's Subtraction Book by Barbara Barbieri McGrath. Charlesbridge Publishing, Inc. 2005.

Relatives Came, The by Cynthia Rylant. Aladdin. 1993.

Shark Swimathon by Stuart J. Murphy. HarperCollins Children's Books. 2001.

Subtraction Action by Loreen Leedy. Holiday House. 2000.

 CHAPTER **7** **Determine the Value of Money**

26 Letters and 99 Cents by Tana Hoban. HarperCollins Children's Books. 1997.

Alexander Who Used to Be Rich Last Sunday by Judith Viorst. Simon & Schuster Children's Publishing Co. 1978.

Go-Around Dollar, The by Barbara Johnston Adams. Simon & Schuster Children's Publishing. 1992.

Jelly Beans for Sale by Bruce Macmillan. Scholastic, Inc. 1996.

Mon$ter Money Book, The by Loreen Leedy. Holiday House. 1992.

Penny Pot, The by Stuart J. Murphy. HarperCollins Children's Books. 1998.

Pigs Will Be Pigs by Amy Axelrod. Simon & Schuster Children's Publishing Co. 1994.

Slugger's Car Wash by Stuart J. Murphy. HarperCollins Children's Books. 2002.

Subtraction Action by Loreen Leedy. Holiday House. 2000.

You Can't Buy a Dinosaur with a Dime by Harriet Ziefert. Handprint Books. 2003.

 CHAPTER **8** **Measure Time and Temperature**

Grouchy Ladybug, The by Eric Carle. HarperCollins Children's Books. 1977.

What's Next, Nina? by Sue Kassirer and Page Eastburn O'Rourke. Kane Press.

Pigs on a Blanket by Amy Axlerod. Simon & Schuster Children's Publishing Co. 1996.

Science Tools by J.A. Randolph. Newbridge Educational Pub. 1999.

Go Fly a Kite! by John Burnstein.

Literature Support

CHAPTER 9 — Model Fractions

Apple Fractions by Jerry Pallotta. Scholastic, Inc. 2002.
Fraction Action by Loreen Leedy. Holiday House. 1994.
Fraction Fun by Jerry Pallotta. Scholastic, Inc. 1996.
Gator Pie by Louise Mathews. Sundance Publishing. 1979.
Hershey's Chocolate Fractions Book, The by Jerry Pallotta. Scholastic, Inc. 2001.
Jump, Kangaroo, Jump by Stuart J. Murphy. Harper Collins Children's Books. 1999.
Piece = Part = Portion by Scott Gifford. Tricycle Press. 2003.
Skittles Riddles Math by Barbara Barbieri McGrath. Charlesbridge Publishing, Inc. 2003.

CHAPTER 10 — Use Place Value to 1,000

512 Ants on Sullivan Street, The by Carol A. Losi. Scholastic, Inc. 1997.
Best Vacation Ever, The by Stuart J. Murphy. HarperCollins Children's Books. 1998.
Case of the Missing Birthday Party, The by Joanne Rocklin. Scholastic, Inc. 1996.
Earth Day—Hooray! by Stuart J. Murphy. HarperCollins Children's Books. 2004.
Fun with Numbers by Massin. Creative Editions. 1995.
History of Counting, The by Denise Schmandt-Besserat. HarperCollins. 1999.
How Much, How Many, How Far, How Heavy, How Long, How Tall Is 1000 by Helen Nolan. Kids Can Press. 2001.
How Much Is a Million? by David M. Schwartz. HarperCollins. 1985.
Just Enough Carrots by Stuart J. Murphy. HarperCollins Children's Books. 1997.
King's Commissioners, The by Aileen Friedman. Scholastic, Inc. 1998.
Less Than Zero by Stuart J. Murphy. HarperCollins Children's Books. 2003.
Out for the Count: A Counting Adventure by Kathryn Cave. Frances Lincoln. 1991.

CHAPTER 11 — Understand Geometric Shapes and Spatial Reasoning

Captain Invincible and the Space Shapes by Stuart J. Murphy. HarperCollins Children's Books. 2001.
Cubes, Cones, Cylinders, & Spheres by Tana Hoban. HarperCollins Children's Books. 2000.
Grandfather Tang's Story by Ann Tompert. Random House Company. 1990.
Greedy Triangle, The by Marilyn Burns. Scholastic, Inc. 1994.
Three Pigs, One Wolf, and Seven Magic Shapes by Grace Maccarone. Scholastic, Inc. 1997.
Twizzlers Pull & Peel Math From Simple Shapes to Geometry by Jerry Pallotta. Scholastic, Inc. 2005.
Village of Round and Square Houses, The by Ann Grifalconi. Little Brown & Company. 1964.

CHAPTER 12 — Measure Length and Area

Super Sand Castle Saturday by Stuart J. Murphy. HarperCollins Children's Books. 1996.
Centipede's 100 shoes by Tony Ross. Henry Holt and Company, LLC. 2002.
Inchworm and a Half by Elinor J. Pinczes. Houghton Mifflin Company. 2001.
Measuring Penny by Loreen Leedy. Holiday House. 1997.
Polly's Pen Pal by Stuart J. Murphy. HarperCollins Children's Books. 2005.
Big, Better, Best by Stuart J. Murphy. HarperCollins Children's Books. 2000.

Measure Capacity and Weight
CHAPTER 13

A House for Birdie by Stuart J. Murphy. HarperCollins Children's Books. 2004.

Pigs in the Pantry by Amy Axelrod. Simon & Schuster Children's Publishing Co. 1997.

How Big is a Foot? by Rolf Myller. Random House. 1991.

Room for Ripley by Stuart J. Murphy. HarperCollins Children's Books. 1999.

How Heavy Is It? by Brian Sargent. Children's Book Press.

If Dogs Were Dinosaurs by David M. Schwartz. Scholastic, Inc. 2005.

Gold Fever by Verla Kay. Penguin Group USA, Inc. 1999.

 Solve Three-Digit Addition and Subtraction Problems
CHAPTER 14

329th Friend, The by Marjorie W. Sharmat. Simon & Schuster Children's Publishing Co. 1979.

Coyotes All Around by Stuart J. Murphy. HarperCollins Children's Books. 2000.

Fun With Roman Numerals by David Adler. HarperCollins Children's Books. 1977.

Alexander Who Used to Be Rich Last Sunday by Judith Viorst. Simon & Schuster Children's Publishing Co. 1978.

Grapes of Math, The by Greg Tang. Scholastic, Inc. 2001.

How Big Were the Dinosaurs? by Bernard Most. Harcourt Brace & Company. 1994.

Math Mini Mysteries by Sandra Markle. Simon & Schuster Children's Publishing Co. 1992.

Panda Math: Learning About Subtraction from Hua Mei Mei Sheng by Ann Whitehead Nagda. Henry Holt and Company, LLC. 2005.

Roman Numerals 1 to MM by Arthur Geisert. Houghton Mifflin Company. 1996.

Shark Swimathon by Stuart J. Murphy. HarperCollins Children's Books. 2001.

Water Hole, The by Graeme Base. Harry N. Abrams. 2001

 Model Multiplication and Division
CHAPTER 15

What Comes in 2s, 3s, and 4s? by Suzanne Aker. Simon & Schuster Children's Publishing Co. 1990.

Spunky Monkeys on Parade by Stuart J. Murphy. HarperCollins Children's Books. 2003.

Too Many Kangaroo Things to Do by Stuart J. Murphy. HarperCollins Children's Books. 1996.

Counting is for the Birds by Frank Mazzola Jr. Charlesbridge Publishing, Inc. 2002.

Zachary Zormer Shape Transformer by Joanne Reisberg. Charlesbridge Publishing, Inc. 2006.

Everybody Wins by Sheila Bruce. Kane Press.

Professional Development

So You're Teaching Second Grade...
An Introduction to the Social, Physical, and Cognitive Development of Second Graders

Teaching second grade is a wonderful and exciting experience that includes observing, listening, and watching children. Not only does the mathematics build on what students have already learned and experienced in earlier grades, but it also continues to set the foundation for all later learning. The most important factor to the successful growth of seven- and eight-year-old children is being able to recognize specific characteristics of a child's development. Knowing and understanding these characteristics can help a teacher implement effective practices in teaching the what, why, and how to a child.

Social Development

It is important to know that each child is an individual, and that the range of abilities and needs in groups of children is likely to be varied in the classroom. To meet these varying abilities and needs, math concepts can be taught through innovative ways with literature, music, and tools that are meaningful to the child. Even though most students at this age prefer to work by themselves and appreciate quiet

time to work alone, they do like to work with partners, especially playing games and using puzzles. Likewise, developing the ability to work in groups comes from sharing and taking turns, trusting, and communication through listening and discussion. Children of this age may also dislike being singled out, even for praise. They do tend to worry, are self-critical, and may express a lack of confidence. Throughout the school year, the teacher should provide many opportunities for children of this age level to develop a positive concept of self and a sense of responsibility, as well as to build relationships with others.

Physical Development

Sometimes second graders have trouble copying from the board because they exhibit myopic tendencies and concentrate on the details in their visual field (Wood, 1994). Even though they often work with a three-fingered pencil grasp that results in small printing, drawing, and number work, their written work does tend to be neat. They do display good understanding of right and left directionality, and they have abilities to focus a bit more and to concentrate on tasks that require more than 15 minutes.

Second Graders at a Glance
- ✔ The classroom is usually quieter than first grade, but transition times for students can be noisy.
- ✔ Most second graders like to know the day's schedule and have adequate time to finish tasks.

- ✔ Students are easily motivated and like to be challenged.
- ✔ Students are by nature curious and interested in discovering how things work.
- ✔ Students should use a hands-on approach to learning foundational concepts.

What Second Graders Should Know

To prepare students for an appropriate and engaging level of rigor in math, most core curriculums outline the following content standards.

Number Sense and Operations
An important feature of number sense for second graders is understanding the base-ten place value system to 1,000, including comparing and ordering whole numbers using the comparative symbols. Students continue work with basic addition and subtraction facts, as well as problems involving money (dollars and cents). By the end of second grade, students understand and use the inverse relationships between addition and subtraction to solve problems flexibly, efficiently, and accurately (to automaticity). In finding sums and differences of whole numbers up to three-digits, students learn the basics of "carrying" and "borrowing," such as exchanging 1 ten for 10 ones and vice versa. In addition, students learn to solve simple concepts of multiplication and division including skip counting of 2s, 5s, and 10s.

Considerations for Grade-Level Accomplishments in Grade Two

- Counting 100 through 999
- Writing numbers
- Borrowing
- Skip counting
- Counting group of coins
- Aligning columns
- Writing numbers
- Borrowing
- Skip counting
- Understanding associativity
- Reviewing time equivalencies
- Understanding money
- Telling time
- Understanding fractions

Students in this grade level also learn about fractions through verbal and written descriptions and begin understanding the concept of equivalence of fractions with pictures.

Patterns, Relationships, and Algebraic Thinking

In this strand, students learn to use the commutative and associative rules to simplify mental calculations. For example, students are expected to know that both properties apply to addition and multiplication, but not to subtraction and division. Also, students are expected to relate addition and subtraction number sentences to problem situations.

Measurement and Geometry

These strands place emphasis on understanding that measurement is based on identifying a unit of measure and then measuring the length of objects by iterating or repeating a nonstandard or standard unit. In terms of measuring time, students are expected to know time equivalencies such as 1 minute equals 60 seconds, and are taught a general procedure for telling time. In geometry, students use attributes to identify and describe common plane and solid geometric shapes.

Statistics, Data Analysis, and Probability

Students are expected to collect, record, organize, display, and interpret data on bar graphs and charts with tallies. Students also should be able to identify and demonstrate patterns and how they grow. As in first grade, students are expected to distinguish between the most likely term and the next term in probability. Students look for likely patterns and the rule or function that generates what is likely to come next.

Problem Solving

In any mathematics curriculum, mathematical reasoning and problem solving are embedded throughout. Reasoning is a process skill that includes basic thinking, critical thinking, and creative thinking. Problem solving and formal and informal reasoning underlie all content areas. Together with other mathematical tools, students use mathematical reasoning to make decisions about how to set up problems, solve them, and evaluate solutions for reasonableness.

The Rewards of Teaching

In essence, the rewards of teaching second grade are immeasurable! Positive learning experiences empower children to think, solve problems, communicate their thinking, and make real-word connections. Remember, to teach is to learn, to learn is to grow, and to grow is believing that each and every child is important in your class.

References

Copley, Juanita V. (2000). *The Young Child and Mathematics*. Washington D.C.: National Association for the Education of Young Children.

McDevitt, Teresa M. & Ormrod, Jeanne Ellis. (2002). *Child Development and Education*. Upper Saddle River, NJ: Pearson Education, Inc.

Sutton, John & Krueger, Alice., Edited by (2002). *EDThoughts: What We Know About Mathematics Teaching and Learning*. Aurora, CO: McREL: Mid-continent Research for Education and Learning

Wood, Chip. (1994). Yardsticks: *Children in the Classroom Ages 4-12*. Greenfield, MA. Northeast Foundation for Children

Principles and Standards for School Mathematics. (2000). Reston, Virginia: The National Council of Teachers of Mathematics, Inc.

Howden, H. (1989). "Teaching Number Sense". *Arithmetic Teacher*, 36(6), p. 6-11

Van De Walle, John A. (2007). *Elementary and Middle School Mathematics Teaching Developmentally (Sixth Edition)*. Pearson Education, Inc.

Van De Walle, John A. & Lovin, LouAnn H. (2006). *Teaching Student-Centered Mathematics, Grade K-3*. Pearson Education, Inc.

Ellen Hatley is a district Instructional Support Teacher for Elementary Mathematics in Austin, Texas. With over 17 years of educational experience, she has written curriculum, provided staff development, and presented at NCTM. Ellen received her undergraduate degree from the University of Texas at Arlington and a Master of Education from Northern Arizona University.

Professional Development

Reaching All Learners: Providing Equity in Mathematics Education

Reaching All Learners makes mathematics understanding and mastery obtainable to all students, and supports teachers and parents as they help students attain that mastery. The goal of Reaching All Learners is to provide every person with ample and equitable opportunities to approach mathematics. When mathematics educators discuss equity in mathematics teaching and learning, their language often includes phrases that include all children, such as "mathematics for all children" or "mathematics opportunity for every child." Inherent in this language is the desire to provide every child high quality mathematics education that will give them access to professions and careers of their choice (Malloy, 2004).

Equity in mathematics education is about access—that is, universal access. However, we have not been successful at achieving measurable equity in achievement, which means that students do not have the opportunity to acquire skills necessary to access 70% of careers of today (Moses, 2001). Schoenfeld discusses the "potential for providing high quality mathematics instruction for all students" (p. 13) from a systemic perspective. He lays out

" Reaching All Learners calls for reasonable and appropriate accommodations to be made to promote access and attainment for all students. "

four systemic conditions that are necessary for achieving this goal: "(a) high quality curriculum; (b) stable, knowledgeable, and professional teaching community; (c) high quality assessment that is aligned with curricular goals; (d) and stability and mechanisms for the evolution of curricula, assessment, and professional development" (Schoenfeld, 2002). These conditions are critical for schools and districts to consider and implement as they progress toward the ultimate goal: ample and equitable opportunities in mathematics.

It Begins With Teachers

Teachers often seek help by going to conferences and attending professional development sessions where they see many activities and investigations that augment the presentation of varied topics, but many teachers do not know how to fully create an effective and equitable classroom culture that offers learning opportunities for all students.

In order for students to have equal access to mathematics, teachers must have strong math backgrounds and instructional skills. They have to be confident in teaching mathematics, and they must have *access* to ongoing staff development that is available when it is needed. Because teachers and students have varied styles of teaching and learning, it is important to recognize that there is no "one" correct way to teach mathematics. Teachers, more than any other single factor, influence what mathematics students learn and if they master the material.

Flexible Instruction

As students are expected to learn at higher levels and to attain higher standards in mathematics, educators must provide all students with the opportunity and support to achieve these higher goals. Reaching All Learners ensures that the needs of each student are addressed in a manner that allows students to use their own personal strengths to attain the goals expected of them. Reaching All Learners does not mean that every student receives the same instruction; rather, it calls for reasonable and appropriate accommodations to be made to promote access and attainment for all students.

Reaching All Learners provides a two-pronged approach to reaching all learners in the classroom. Reaching All Learners addresses the different learning styles all students bring to the learning process. Reaching All Learners addresses the needs of special student populations, including students of different learning abilities, gifted students, IEP students, and speakers of different languages. Teachers must be able to *differentiate* instruction for students of varied learning styles, prior experiences, interests, socialization needs, and comfort zones (Benjamin, 2005) and abilities.

Getting Parents Involved

Emphasizing parental involvement at home in math learning is another aspect of Reaching All Learners. Research has shown that the more parents are involved with their children's learning, the more successful children are in school (U.S. Department of Education, 1994). Reaching All Learners can help parents understand the skills and procedures used by their children in mathematics learning. To ensure Reaching All Learners, activities that are easy to follow and use everyday materials, are an ideal bridge between the classroom and home environments. Such materials must be informative, useful, and easy for parents to use.

Reaching All Learners: A Two-Pronged Approach

✔ Reaching All Learners addresses the different learning styles all students bring to the learning process.
✔ Reaching All Learners addresses the needs of special student populations, including students of different learning abilities, gifted students, IEP students, and speakers of different languages.

Making Reaching All Learners Work

Equity is a key aspect of learning and understanding. *All* students can learn math, *all* teachers can successfully teach math, and *all* parents can support math learning at home—the key is to make mathematics *accessible to all.*

Reaching All Learners helps to guide parents in their efforts with their children, making them more productive (Epstein, 1994). Reaching All Learners is designed to help students attain mathematical standards, help teachers gain a broader understanding of mathematics, and help parents support their children at home. If all students, teachers, and parents are to be involved in mathematics, a mathematics program must be equitable and accessible.

References

Benjamin, A. *Differentiated instruction using technology.* Larchmont, NY: Eye on Education, 2005.

Epstein, Joyce L. "Theory to Practice: School and Family Partnerships Lead to School Improvement," in *School, Family, and Community Interaction: A View from the Firing Lines,* edited by Cheryl L. Fagnano and Beverly Z. Werver, Boulder, CO: Westview Press, 1994. 32–52.

Malloy, C. E. "Equity in mathematics education is about access." Eds. R. Rubenstein and G. Bright. *2004 NCTM Yearbook: Effective mathematics teaching.* Reston, VA: NCTM, 2004. 1–14.

Moses, R. P., & Cobb, Jr., C. E. *Radical equations: Math literacy and civil rights.* Boston: Beacon Press, 2001.

Schoenfeld, A. "Making mathematics work for all children: Issues of standards, testing, and equity." *Educational Research,* 31. 2002. 13–25.

U.S. Department of Education. *Goals 2000: A World-Class Education for Every Child.* Washington D.C.: U.S. Government Printing Office, 1994.

Carol E. Malloy is Associate Professor in Mathematics Education in the School of Education at the University of North Carolina at Chapel Hill. She teaches secondary mathematics methods courses, mathematics courses for middle and elementary pre-service students, and graduate courses in curriculum and foundations. Carol was a member of the NCTM Board of Directors 1998–2002, NCTM Standards 2000 writing team, and president of the Benjamin Banneker Association. She has 20 years teaching experience in public schools across the United States.

Professional Development

Professional Development

English Learners and Mathematics: Best Practices for Effective Instruction

Anecdotal information from classroom teachers as well as evidence from research has demonstrated that the trend toward using more language in mathematics has seriously affected the achievement of students whose first language is not English. In response to this, the National Council of Teachers of Mathematics (NCTM) emphasizes communication "as an essential part of mathematics and mathematics education" and that "second-language learners in particular need to have opportunities and be given encouragement and support for speaking, writing, reading and listening in mathematics classes." Such efforts have the potential to help second-language learners overcome barriers that will facilitate "communicating to learn mathematics and learning to communicate mathematically" (NCTM, 2000).

Research done on effective mathematics instruction for English Learners (ELs) has identified the following best practices. These can be categorized as cultural, instructional and linguistic.

Cultural Considerations

Be aware of how children's home cultures and previous experiences can contribute to their mathematics learning (Gonzalez, et al., 1995; Tikunoff, 1985). ELs bring rich, although often different, experiences with them into the classroom. Consult with bilingual staff and other cultural brokers to find out what

those experiences may be. Then use your students' prior knowledge to create contexts for instruction that are meaningful to them (Garrison & Mora, 1999). This is especially important when students are asked to solve word problems, for in order to do so, they need to be able to picture and understand the situation. This is extremely difficult to do if their experiences do not allow them to visualize what the problem is about.

" ELs bring rich, although often different, experiences with them into the classroom. Consult with bilingual staff and other cultural brokers to find out what those experiences may be. "

Instructional Considerations

Teaching the concept before the math can help ELs conceptualize what they are learning without having to master the language first (Khisty & Viego, 1999). This

can be through the use of pictures, video, manipulatives, realia (actual objects instead of just pictures or models), games, and graphic organizers (Krashen, 1981; Garrison & Mora, 1999). In addition to using these kinesthetic and visual/spatial approaches to teaching concepts, it is important to also encourage students to learn from each other. Working out problems with the aid of peers instead of individually supports the learning styles of many students who come from cultures in which collaborative learning is the norm rather than the exception.

Linguistic Considerations

If teachers structure classroom activities so that students have to speak and write about mathematics, there will be multiple opportunities to use the language of mathematics (Gee, 1992). This is best done if the teacher engages students in instructional conversations that include the use of questions (Khisty & Viego, 1999), collaboration and group work

Vocabulary Word	Common Meaning	Mathematical Meaning
table	piece of furniture often used for eating	visual representation of data
foot	appendage at the end of one's leg	standard unit of measurement equal to 12 inches
problem	situation that is difficult to resolve	Math exercise

(Garrison & Mora, 1999). It is also important that while talking about mathematics students be encouraged to use the technical language associated with it once the concept is learned – for example, using "minus" instead of "take away" and including terms such as quotient, dividend, and divisor.

Other vocabulary that needs to be explicitly addressed are terms that can have both mathematical and common meanings. A table can be a piece of furniture, but in mathematics it often refers to a visual representation of data. Round, square, foot, and problem are other examples of such terms. As you are planning lessons, note these words and make sure that ELs understand that the common meaning is different than the technical.

In addition to vocabulary there are numerous other language features that can be problematic for ELs in the mathematics classroom. Seek out the language experts at your school, bilingual teachers and aides and teachers of English as a second language, to collaborate about how these challenges can be addressed.

Unique Needs

In order to ensure that all students achieve to their potential, Reaching All Learners stresses that teachers address the unique needs of each student in the classroom in a way that capitalizes on their strengths to meet educational goals. Best practices, such as those given above, and reasonable accommodations need to be made to promote access and achievement in mathematics for all students (Mathematics Framework for California Public Schools, 2006).

References:

California State Board of Education. (2006). *Mathematics Framework for California Public Schools.* Sacramento, CA: California State Board of Education.

Garrison, L & Mora, J. K. (1999). Adapting mathematics instruction for English language learners: The language-concept connection. In *National Council of Teachers of Mathematics. Changing the faces of mathematics: Perspectives on Latinos* (pp. 35-47). Reston VA: National Council of Teachers of Mathematics.

Gee, J. P. (1992). *The social mind, language, ideology, and social practice.* New York: Bergin & Garvey.

Gonzales, N., et al. (1995). Funds of knowledge for teaching in Latino households. *Urban Education*, 29(4) 443-470.

Khisty, L. L. & Viego, G. (1999). Challenging conventional wisdom: A case study. In *National Council of Teachers of Mathematics. Changing the faces of mathematics: Perspectives on Latinos* (pp. 35–47). Reston VA: National Council of Teachers of Mathematics.

Krashen, S. (1981). *Second language acquisition and second language learning.* London: Pergamon Press.

National Council of Teachers of Mathematics (NCTM). (2000). *Principles and standards for school mathematics.* Reston: VA: National Council of Teachers of Mathematics. 60.

Tikunoff, W. (1985). Applying significant bilingual instructional features in the classroom. Part C Bilingual Education Research Series. Rosslyn, VA: National Clearinghouse for Bilingual Education. (ERIC Document Reproduction Service No. ED 338 106).

Kathryn Heinze teaches in the Graduate School of Education at Hamline University in St. Paul, Minnesota. Since receiving an M.A. in ESL from the University of Minnesota, she has spent thirty years in the classroom as an ESL teacher and teacher educator. Recently, she has focused on helping teachers make mathematics instruction more accessible to ELs.

Professional Development

Professional Development

Data-Driven Decision Making

Using Assessment to Inform Instruction and Improve Student Achievement

As mathematics educators, we understand the importance of assessment to the mathematics teaching/learning process. Assessment is an important and essential tool for teachers to use to improve instruction. In fact, it is assessment that truly distinguishes between teaching and learning. But what is it that distinguishes effective assessment from routine, calendar-based assessment? How does a teacher ensure that assessment informs teaching in a meaningful way, one that consistently shapes students learning?

Put simply, it requires data-driven decision making based on an ongoing assessment cycle. Teachers need to take the data collected from their students' performance on various assessments and use this data to make decisions on next steps for instruction.

The Assessment Cycle

To be truly effective, assessment must be embedded in the teaching and learning process, not just administered out of context at set intervals during the school year. Ongoing assessment helps teachers fine-tune the teaching process to ensure student understanding of mathematical concepts. Assessment must gather a bounty of information in order to help teachers measure student progress and glean students' potential. To this end, teachers should strive to keep accurate and dated information on their

students' progress in mathematics throughout the learning process.

Consider the following three stages of the assessment cycle:

- **Stage 1:** Identify what is to be taught, how it will be taught, and how to assess student learning.
- **Stage 2:** Gather evidence of student learning, interpret student responses, and record data.
- **Stage 3:** Act on the results. How does the data impact my teaching methods? What concepts need to be retaught?

The implementation of these types of assessments across all grade levels will help guide instruction and also provide a road map that leads students to mastery of core curriculum concepts and skills.

Assessment	
Stage 1	Do students possess crucial prerequisite skills and knowledge? Do students already know some of the material that is to be taught?
Stage 2	Are students progressing adequately toward achieving the standards?
Stage 3	Have students achieved the goals defined by a given standard of a group of standards?

Forms of Assessment

In order to effectively measure mathematical learning, teachers must make sure we include various forms of assessment. A complete assessment program should include multiple measures:

Diagnostic: The purpose of a diagnostic assessment is to determine whether the student has the skills and knowledge necessary to begin the chapter, or if the student needs intervention prior to beginning the chapter.

Formative: Daily formative assessment should include scaffolding questions as well as talking, thinking, and writing about mathematics.

Summative: Summative assessment helps the teacher determine whether the students have learned the material that they were taught throughout the chapter.

Assessment to Guide Instruction

Assessment allows the teacher to consider the strengths and challenges of students; the effectiveness of the mathematics curriculum; and the next steps that should be taken in the instructional process. Some ways to use assessment to guide instruction are:

✔ Pose a "Talk About It" question during a lesson. Encourage students to work in small groups, discussing possible solutions to the question.
✔ Probe for prior knowledge before the introduction of a new concept.
✔ Observe students while they are working either in groups or individually which will give you information regarding their understanding of mathematics.
✔ Conduct student interviews which will offer an opportunity to use questioning strategies to explore an individual student's understanding of a concept.

Assessment: A Complete System

Assessment comes in many forms: diagnostic, formative, and summative. True assessment is dynamic and rich with information concerning student potential and performance. Assessment is the contributing force in improving the teaching and learning of mathematics for all students.

It is the most effective way to distinguish between teaching and learning, both in the classroom and at the district or state level.

References:

Long, Donna. *Using Test Results to Inform Instruction and Improve Student Achievement,* Eisenhower National Clearinghouse, January, 2003.

National Council of Teachers of Mathematics (NCTM). *Mathematics Assessment: A Practical Handbook,* Reston, VA, 2003.

Wahlstrom, Deborah. *Using DATA to Improve Student Achievement,* Successline Inc., 1999.

 **Donna Long** is currently the Elementary Mathematics Marketing Manager for Macmillan/McGraw-Hill. She has served as the National Mathematics Consultant for Macmillan/McGraw-Hill, the National Mathematics Assessment Consultant for CTB/McGraw-Hill, and the Mathematics/Title I Coordinator, Grades K-12, for an urban school district in Indianapolis, Indiana. She has also served as the Mathematics Program Coordinator for Curriculum and Assessment at the Indiana Department of Education.

Entry-Level Assessment **Diagnostic**	Determine whether students have the skills and knowledge necessary to be successful in subsequent lessons.
Progress Monitoring **Formative**	Include various forms of daily assessment such as talking, thinking, and writing about mathematics.
Summative Evaluation **Summative**	Determine whether students have mastered the material they were taught.

Professional Development

Intervention: Bridging the Gaps in Student Learning

It is rare to find an elementary classroom where all of the students are on the same level in mathematics. Often when standards change or students are not at the same level in mathematics, teachers feel the need to push through the mathematics curriculum, even if students are lacking prerequisite skills necessary to succeed. Teaching new mathematics standards to elementary students is analogous to teaching students to swim: expecting students to instantly rise to the rigor of new standards, without bridging the gaps between the old and new standards, sets students up for failure.

In the opinion of many experts in the field, many mathematics programs have provided "inadequate textbooks and inadequate instruction" (Wu, 1998). To avoid such mistakes again, a successful program must provide a systematic way for teachers to bridge the mathematical gaps of students who are accustomed to less rigorous standards. For these reasons, all mathematics programs need to supply teachers with effective tools they can use for assessment and instruction of prerequisite skills.

Entry-Level Assessment: Identifying the Gaps

To accurately inform teaching decisions in the classroom, entry-level, or diagnostic, assessment should be given to students before each chapter. Entry-level assessment should not test new content; it should only test for skills required to proceed successfully into the new content. Such a test helps teachers determine what prerequisite skills students do understand and what skills need to be strengthened before proceeding into the new content. Entry-level assessment should not merely be given and then set aside; the results of entry-level assessment should be used to guide instruction throughout a chapter.

After completing this diagnostic assessment, an effective mathematics program provides different types of intervention and support for different students: intensive, strategic, benchmark, and above-level.

Intensive Intervention

This level of intervention is for students who are two or more years behind grade-level in mathematics. They need intensive instruction provided in an environment outside of the normal classroom for at least 2 hours per day. Ideally, these skill building lessons will not merely be worksheets distributed to students for independent, repetitive practice. And, they should not be merely row after row of exercises.

Intensive intervention should be designed to reteach concepts and skills, thus improving every student's mathematical understanding and procedures. Skill building lessons that are visual and require minimal amounts of reading enable students to work on their own.

" Teaching new mathematics standards to elementary students is analogous to teaching students to swim: expecting students to instantly rise to the rigor of new standards, without bridging the gaps between the old and new standards, sets students up for failure. "

Stepped out models and guided practice of strategies to help students bridge their skill gaps should be provided, before students practice independently. Manipulative activities and games are greatly useful in sustaining interest and engagement during this relearning stage. By following such a structure, students can learn the concepts, skills, and procedures they were lacking.

Strategic Intervention

Students at this level are struggling but still on grade-level. With sustained attention and guidance, a teacher can help lift a student back to the benchmark level without intensive intervention. McGraw-Hill's *Strategic Intervention Guide* provides a complete lesson plan, including goals, questions, and activities that complement the skill building page the students are using. Further, and most importantly, it provides follow up diagnosis and further intervention for students who, having completed the skill builder, still lack the mathematical skills they need to progress.

Benchmark and Above-Level Students

At the same time, students who do have the required prerequisite skills need to be appropriately challenged so they are continually improving their mathematical understanding and do not become bored. For students who do have the necessary prerequisite skills to continue onto new math concepts, skill building activities are not the answer. These on level and advanced students benefit from activities providing a variety of math challenges and experiences they can work on independently. Whenever possible, the teacher should strive to give these students dedicated time as well. Students should be asked higher order thinking questions about the concepts (horizontal) and be challenged with the next grade level's curriculum (vertical).

Summary

Because of the sequential nature of mathematics, when students have deficiencies in their understanding of previous areas of emphasis, it becomes extremely difficult for them to understand new topics that are based on those understandings. Teachers can use entry-level tests, especially when the standards expected of the students have become more rigorous, and then use the results to inform instruction. "It is important that teachers go beyond simply calculating a score to examine each child's response to each item" (Cathcart, 19XX). Students and teachers need to work together to build skills that are lacking by reteaching necessary prerequisite skills. A solid mathematics program will provide entry-level tests and skill building activities based on the test items to enable students to bridge the gaps so they can move forward successfully.

References

California State Board of Education. Mathematics Framework for California Public Schools. Sacramento, CA: California State Board of Education, 2006.

Cathcart, W. George, Yvonne M. Pothier, James H. Vance, and Nadine S. Bezuk. Learning Mathematics in Elementary and Middle Schools. Columbus: Ohio: Prentice Hall, 2000.

Selby, Alan M. "Mathematics from Primary School to College." Mathematics Curriculum Notes, Volume 1B, August 1997.

Van De Walle, John. Elementary and Middle School Mathematics: Teaching Developmentally. White Plains, NY: Addison Wesley Longman, Inc., 1997.

Wu, H. "The Mathematics Education Reform: What is it and why should you care?" www.math.berkeley.edu/~wu/, 1998.

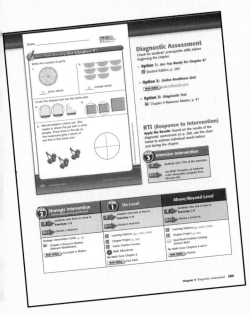

Robyn Silbey is a 30-plus year veteran of Montgomery County Public Schools in Maryland, currently working as a math content coach. She holds an M.S. in Elementary Mathematics Education from McDaniel College and a B.S. in Elementary Education from the University of Maryland. Robyn is a national consultant and serves as a teacher consultant in the Teaching Training Corps for the U.S. Department of Education.

Professional Development

What Does a CGI Classroom Look Like? An Introduction to Cognitively Guided Instruction

Cognitively Guided Instruction, often abbreviated as CGI, is an approach to teaching mathematics that builds on children's natural problem-solving strategies. Based on over 20 years of research, CGI identifies specific strategies students use to help teachers understand how students think so that they can guide them toward mathematical understanding. So, you may ask, what does a CGI classroom actually look like?

Differences on the Surface

Pretend for a moment that you are observing three teachers all of whom are teaching the first-grade concept of subtraction using CGI. The first thing you would likely notice is that each has her or his classroom arranged differently. One teacher has students sitting at tables of four so that students can talk as they work. Another teacher has students sitting first on the carpet in a circle, and then allows them to spread out all over the room to work on problems individually in their math notebooks. The third teacher sits with a small group of students at a problem-solving center who share their strategies with each other. Obviously, using a CGI approach does not involve a particular class configuration.

In these classrooms, teachers pose different types of story problems to introduce subtraction. One teacher has addition and subtraction problems mixed together. Another teacher is using subtraction problems only, while the third teacher is using what appear to be missing-addend problems as well as more traditional subtraction problems. So, CGI does not use a pre-specified set of problems in a given sequence to teach the curriculum. Teachers who use CGI are not limited to specific resources, either. One teacher might read a children's book to provide context for the story problems. Another could refer to a recent field trip to a city park. A third might use a textbook as a teaching resource.

Similarities Underneath

Despite these differences, you would notice several important similarities. As we saw, all of these teachers use story problems to introduce a topic. Further, these teachers would not show the children how to solve these problems. In fact, teachers who use CGI usually tell the children to solve the problems any way they can. They also encourage students to use any tools they want, in a way that makes sense to them and that they can explain or show to another child, or to the teacher. When observing this for the first time, many teachers are mildly surprised that children have so much to say about math.

This may be surprising because so many of us rely on teacher's explanations and demonstrations to teach a concept or skill. This scenario reverses the usual order of instruction that many teachers follow. First, children solve problems and develop meaning for addition and subtraction.

" These teachers know that children are able to solve story problems without direct instruction on strategies, because children naturally direct model story situations about which they have informal knowledge."

> *" Perhaps the most striking feature of CGI is that these teachers have a sense of ownership of this knowledge of children's thinking. It empowers them to make decisions, often on the spot."*

Then, they learn to write number sentences to represent addition and subtraction.

The Teacher's Role in CGI

CGI teacher use their knowledge of problem types and solution strategies to make decisions about their curriculum. This knowledge helps them determine what each child understands and then decide how to help the child extend their understanding. These teachers know that children are able to solve story problems without direct instruction on strategies, because children naturally direct model story situations about which they have informal knowledge.

For example, consider the following problem, called a "Separate Result Unknown" problem.
Jennifer has 17 pieces of candy. She gave 8 of the pieces of candy to her brother. How many pieces of candy does Jennifer have left?

Initially, most children use a tool such as cubes (or tallies or counters) to direct model this situation. They count out 17 cubes, remove 8 of them to show the candies that went to Jennifer's brother, and then count the number of cubes left. However, students may also apply more advanced strategies such as counting back from 17 to 8. They might even count up from 8 to 17 or derive 17 − 8 by figuring 17 − 7, which is 10, and then 10 − 1, which is 9.

CGI and the Benefit to Teachers

When you talk to the teachers about what they are going to do the next day, along with their mathematical goals, you hear them talking about the things they heard their students express and the strategies they saw their students use. They know what these strategies tell them about children's understanding of addition and subtraction.

Perhaps most the striking feature of CGI is that these teachers have a sense of ownership of this knowledge of children's thinking. It empowers them to make decisions, often on the spot. They know when to push, when to hold back, and how to make a problem easier or harder. They know how to support children to make sense of problems in their own ways. They know when to use a story problem and when not to. They know what problems to give next to support children's learning. They know how to listen. Most importantly, they say their curriculum is never quite the same from one year to the next, because the problems they pose depend on the children in their class.

Additional Reading:

Carpenter, T. P., Ansell, E., Franke, M. L., Fennema, E. & Weisbeck, L. (1993). Models of problem solving: A study of kindergarten children's problem-solving processes. *Journal for Research in Mathematics Education, 24*(5), 427-440.

Carpenter, T. P., Fennema, E., Franke, M., Levi, L. & Empson, S. B. (1999). *Children's Mathematics: Cognitively Guided Instruction.* Portsmouth, NH: Heinemann.

Carpenter, T. P., Fennema, E., Franke, M., Levi, L. & Empson, S. B. (2000). *Cognitively Guided Instruction: A Research-Based Teacher Professional Development Program for Elementary Mathematics.* Research Report 003. Madison, WI: National Center for Improving Student Learning and Achievement in Mathematics and Science.

Carpenter, T. P., Franke, M., & Levi, L. (2003). *Thinking mathematically: Integrating Arithmetic and Algebra in Elementary School.* Portsmouth, NH: Heinemann.

Susan B. Empson is an Associate Professor of Science and Mathematics Education at The University of Texas at Austin. She earned her Ph.D. in Mathematics Education at the University of Wisconsin-Madison and has worked on the Cognitively Guided Instruction project. Her research has been supported by the National Science Foundation and the Spencer Foundation, and published in such journals as *Cognition and Instruction, Journal for Research in Mathematics Education, Teaching Children Mathematics,* and *Journal of Mathematics Teacher Education.*

Professional Development

Professional Development

Literature and Math: Suggestions for Implementing Literature in Your Math Instruction

The level of excitement was palpable in every classroom, corridor, and office of the elementary school I was visiting for an assembly program about my mathematical children's books. Inspired by *How Much Is a Million?*, the students decided to surprise me with a collection of one million popcorn kernels. However, they did far more than simply gather heaps of corn. They predicted, they estimated, they calculated. They kept track of their progress through graphs and tables. They raised mathematical questions, solved mathematical problems, and thought mathematically.

Young children answered questions like, "If we each bring in 10 popcorn kernels, how many will we contribute?" Older students wrote out five and six digit numbers, discussing place value. Teachers asked "How many more do we need before we have a million?" Older students solved problems like, "If

we keep collecting corn at this rate, how long will it take to reach a million?" or "If 1,000 kernels fill this container, how large of a container will we need to hold a million?"

Now, after weeks of collecting corn and discussing the mathematics involved, everyone would get to see one million kernels today! The final 100 kernels were counted in unison by everyone in the school led by the principal over the PA system: "…999,997…999,998…999,999 …1,000,000!!!" The building rocked with cheers.

Making the Connection

Is it possible to get this level of excitement in your classroom, or even your entire school, all from the inspiration of a children's book? Certainly! *How Much Is a Million?* is a simple book that gets readers to visualize the magnitude of the numbers one million, one billion, and one trillion. It is written for young children, but it has been used by teachers of grades ranging from preschool through high school. The possibilities for using it are as vast as the numbers themselves.

How Much Is a Million? is certainly not the only book that has been used by teachers to help teach mathematics. Children's books are finding their way into the math classroom as teachers see the benefits of augmenting their mathematical teaching through literature. "To me, literature has always been

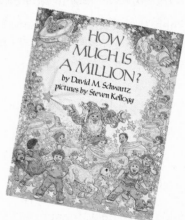

the key to kids' learning," says veteran teacher and Presidential Award Winner Kathy Reed. "From a very young age, children love books but they don't necessarily come to school with a love of mathematics. Through literature, I can take the inherent love kids have for books and tie it to math. A good book can bring the math lesson I'm teaching right into their world."

"Mathematics is a natural communication system that we can use to describe our world and communicate our experiences," according to David J. Whitin and Sandra Wilde (Whitin and Wilde, 2000). By sharing mathematical literature with students, teachers can foster not only vocabulary development but also the expression and comprehension of thoughts in mathematical terms. Discussion of the mathematical ideas in books can help teachers assess students' prior knowledge and address misconceptions.

Where to Begin?

The first task for a teacher interested in using literature in the math classroom is to select the book most appropriate for the task. One place to start is in McGraw-Hill's *Math Connects.* You will find optional literature connections for each lesson, all supported by teaching strategies and activities that connect to the lesson concept.

Teachers who want to choose their own literature should consider several criteria. Select books that:

✔ Both children and teachers will enjoy. A good book for mathematical literature is a good book—period.

✔ Inspire children's natural curiosity, ignite their imaginations, and encourage them to ask questions or respond in varied ways. By contrast, avoid didactic books that merely dress up a math lesson with pictures and/or a contrived storyline.

✔ Present the mathematics soundly and with visual representations that are accurate and inviting. Watch out for books in which the author employs math gimmicks.

✔ Have strong cross-curricular connections to science, social studies, art, music, and other areas of the curriculum. Through these books, students will come to appreciate the broad reach of mathematics.

Tips for Using Literature with Math

- Read the book aloud, cover to cover, for its own enjoyment. Return to it in a second reading to pull the math out of it.
- Look for just one math lesson at a time even if a book has many. You can always revisit it at another time to help with additional math concepts.
- Be open to student questions and comments—they may lead to an appropriate math lesson.
- Prepare by assembling manipulatives appropriate to the story you plan to read.

A Final Lesson

After reading *If You Made a Million,* a teacher told me she asked her students to explore one statement from the book. Working together, two students decided to refute my assertion that a million dollars in quarters would weigh as much as a whale. In a multi-step process involving multiplication and division, the students showed that a 60-ton blue whale would weigh as much as two and a half million dollars worth of quarters. They then wrote to tell me about my "mistake."

To me, it was not important whether I erred or they had misinterpreted my words. More importantly, the book had piqued their curiosity, inspired them to develop a mathematical strategy to solve a complex problem, and honed their basic math skills along the way. What more could a teacher hope for?

" Through literature, I can take the inherent love kids have for books and tie it to math. A good book can bring the math lesson I'm teaching right into their world."

Presidental Award Winner Kath Reed

References:

Schwartz, David. *If You Made a Million.* HarperTrophy, 1994.

Schwartz, David. *If You Hopped Like a Frog.* Scholastic Press, 1999.

Schwartz, David. *How Much is a Million.* HarperTrophy, 2005.

Whitin, David J. and Wilde, Sandra. *Read Any Good Math Lately? Children's Books for Mathematical Learning, K-6.* Heinemann, 1992. 6.

David M. Schwartz is the author of many children's books that make math come alive as well as a popular speaker for both children and educators. His books include *How Much is a Million?, If You Made a Million, G is for Googol,* and *If You Hopped Like a Frog.* You can learn more about David at www.davidschwartz.com.

Selected Research Bibliography

General Resources

Bransford, J. D., A. L. Brown, R. R. Cocking, et al. *How People Learn: Brain, Mind, Experience, and School*. Washington, DC: National Academy Press, 2000. 24.

Grouws, Douglas A. ed. *Handbook of Research on Mathematics Teaching*. New York: Maxwell Macmillan, 1992.

National Research Council. *Adding It Up: Helping Children Learn Mathematics*. Eds. J. Kilpatrick, J. Swafford, and B. Findell. Washington, DC: National Academy Press, 2001.

National Research Council. *How Students Learn: History, Mathematics, and Science in the Classroom*. Eds. M. S. Donovan and J. D. Bransford. Washington, DC: National Academy Press, 2002.

Reys, Robert E., Mary M. Lindquist, Diana V. Lambdin, Marilyn N. Suydam, Nancy L. Smith. *Helping Children Learn Mathematics*. 7th Ed. TK: Wiley, 2003.

Selby, A. M. "Mathematics from Primary School to College." *Mathematics Curriculum Notes*. 1B (Aug 1997).

Senk, S. L. and D.R. Thompson, eds. *Standards-Based School Mathematics Curricula: What Does the Research Say about Student Outcomes?* Hillsdale: Lawrence Erlbaum Associates, Inc., 2003.

Sutton, J. and A. Krueger, eds. *EDThoughts: What We Know About Mathematics Teaching and Learning*. Aurora: Mid-continent Research for Education and Learning, 2002.

Van de Walle, John A. *Elementary and Middle School Mathematics: Teaching Developmentally*. 3rd Ed. New York: Longman, 1998.

Assessment

Black, P. and D. William. "Inside the Black Box: Raising Standards through Classroom Assessment." *Phi Delta Kappan* (Oct 1998): 139-148.

Cobb, Paul, Terry Wood, Erna Yackel, John Nicholls, Grayson Wheatley, Beatriz Trigatti, and Marcella Perlwitz. "Assessment of a Problem-Center Second-Grade Mathematics Project." *Journal for Research in Mathematics Education* 22 (Jan 1991): 3-29.

Newmann, F. M., A. S. Bryk, and J. K. Nagoka. *Authentic Intellectual Work and Standardized Tests: Conflict or Coexistence?* Chicago: Consortium on Chicago School Research, 2001.

Stenmark, J. K. *Mathematics Assessment: Myths, Models, Good Questions, and Practical Suggestions*. Berkeley: University of California, 1989.

Differentiated Instruction

Banks, J. A. *Cultural Diversity and Education: Foundations, Curriculum and Teaching*. 4th Ed. *Multiethnic Education: Theory and Practice*. Boston: Allyn and Bacon, 2001.

Baroody, Arthur J. "An Investigative Approach to the Mathematics Instruction of Children Classified as Learning Disabled." Eds. D. Kim Reid, Wayne P. Hresko, and H. Lee Swanson. *Cognitive Approaches to Learning Disabilities*. Austin: Pro-Ed, 1996. 547-615.

Brimijoin, K., E. Marquisee, and C. Tomlinson. "Using Data to Differentiate Instruction. *Educational Leadership* 60:5 (Feb 2003): 70-72.

Kulik, J. A. *An Analysis of the Research on Ability Grouping: Historical and Contemporary Perspectives*. Storrs: The National Research Center on the Gifted and Talented, 1992.

Loveless, T. "The Tracking and Ability Grouping Debate." *Fordham Report* 2:8 (1998).

Tomlinson, C. "The Mobius Effect: Addressing Learner Variance in Schools." *Journal of Learning Disabilities* 37:6 (2004): 516-524.

Tomlinson, C. A., C. Brighton, H. Hertberg, C. M. Callahan, T. R. Moon, K. Brimijoin, L. A. Conover, and T. Reynolds. "Differentiating Instruction in Response to Student Readiness, Interest, and Learning Profile in Academically Diverse Classroom: A Review of Literature." *Journal for the Education of the Gifted* 27 (2003): 119-145.

English-Language Learners

Mohan, B. The Second Language as a Medium of Learning. Eds. B. Mohan, C. Leung, and C. Davison. *English as a Second Language in the Mainstream*. Harlow, UK: Longman, 2001. 107-126.

Snow, M. A., M. Met, and F. Genesee. "A Conceptual Framework for the Integration of Language and Content in Second/Foreign Language Instruction. *TESOL Quarterly* 23:2 (1989): 201-217.

Swain, M. "Integrating Language and Content in Immersion Classrooms: Research Perspectives." *The Canadian Modern Language Review* 52:4 (1996): 529-548.

Research Bibliography

Foldables™/Graphic Organizers

Alvermann, D. E. and P. R. Boothby. "Children's Transfer of Graphic Organizer Instruction." *Reading Psychology* 7:2 (1986): 87-100

Armbruster, B. B., T. H. Anderson, and J. Ostertag. "Does Text Structure/Summarization Instruction Facilitate Learning from Expository Text." *Reading Research Quarterly* 22:3 (1987): 331-346.

Darch, C. B., D. W. Carnine, and E. J. Kameenui. "The Role of Graphic Organizers and Social Structure in Content Area Instruction." *Journal of Reading Behavior* 18:4 (1986): 275-295.

Mayer, R. E. "Can Advance Organizers Influence Meaningful Learning?" *Review of Educational Research* 49 (1979): 371-383.

Mayer, R. E. "Models of Understanding." *Review of Educational Research* 59:1 (1989): 43-64.

Robinson, D. H., and D. A. Kiewra. "Visual Argument: Graphic Organizers are Superior to Outlines in Improving Learning from Text." *Journal of Educational Psychology* 87:3 (1996): 455-467.

Instructional Strategies

Carpenter, T. P., E. Fennema, M. L. Franke, L. Levi, and S. E. Empson. *Children's Mathematics: Cognitively Guided Instruction*. Westport: Heinemann, 1999.

Ericsson, K. A., R. T. Krampe, and C. Tesch- Romer. "The Role of Deliberate Practice in the Acquisition of Expert Performance," *Psychological Review* 100 (1993).

Gottfried, G. M. "Using Metaphors as Modifiers: Children's Production of Metaphoric Compounds." *Journal of Child Language* 24:3 (1998): 567-601.

Hiebert, J., T. P. Carpenter, E. Fennema, K. C. Fuson, H. Murray, A. Olivier, P. Human, and D. Wearner. *Making Sense: Teaching and Learning Mathematics with Understanding*. Portsmouth: Heinemann, 1997.

Jones, B., A. Palincsar, D. Ogle, and E. Carr. *Strategic Teaching and Learning: Cognitive Instruction in the Content Areas*. Alexandria: Association for Supervision and Curriculum Development, 1987.

Mason, L. "Cognitive and Metacognitive Aspects in Conceptual Change by Analogy." *Instructional Science* 22:3 (1994): 157-187.

Newby, T. J., P. A. Ertmer, and D. A. Stepich. "Instructional Analogies and the Learning of Concepts." *Educational Technology Research and Development* 43:1 (1995): 5-18.

Ripoll, T. "Why This Made Me Think of That." *Thinking and Reasoning* 4:1 (1999): 15-43.

Rosenshine, B. and C. C. Meister. "Reciprocal Teaching: A Review of the Research." *Review of Educational Research* 64:4 (1994): 479-530.

Rosenshine, B., C. Meister, S. Chapman. "Teaching Students to Generate Questions: A Review of the Intervention Studies." *Review of Educational Research* 66:2 (1996): 181-221.

Ross, B. H. "This is Like That: The Use of Earlier Problems and the Separation of Similarity Effects." *Journal of Experimental Psychology* 13:4 (1987): 629-639.

Selby, Alan M. "Mathematics from Primary School to College." *Mathematics Curriculum Notes* 1B (Aug 1997).

Sowell, E. J. "Effects of Manipulative Materials in Mathematics Instruction." *Journal for Research in Mathematics Education* 20:5 (1989): 498-505

Trafton, P. R. "Toward More Effective, Efficient Instruction in Mathematics." *Elementary School Journal* 84:5 (1984): 514-528.

Mathematical Content

Anghileri, J. and D. C. Johnson. "Arithmetic Operations on Whole Numbers: Multiplication and Division." *Teaching Mathematics in Grades K-8*. Boston: Allyn and Bacon, 1992. 157-200.

Behr, M. J. and T. R. Post. "Teaching Rational Number and Decimal Concepts." *Teaching Mathematics in Grades K-8: Research Based Methods*. Boston: Allyn and Bacon, 1992.

Brodie, J. P. *Constructing Ideas about Large Numbers*. TK: Creative Publications, 1995.

Clements, D. *Learning and Teaching Measurement*. Ralston: NCTM, 2003.

Edwards, Edgar L., Jr., ed. *Algebra for Everyone*. Ralston: NCTM, 1990.

Franco, B., et al. *Understanding Geometry*. TK: Great Source Education Group, 1998.

Fuson, K. C. and K.T. Brinko. "Research on Whole Number Addition and Subtraction." *Handbook of Research on Teaching and Learning*. New York: Macmillan, 1992. 243-275.

Hoffer, A. R. and S. A. K. Hoffer. "Ratios and Proportional Thinking." *Teaching Mathematics in Grades K-8: Research Based Methods*. Boston: Allyn and Bacon, 1992.

Isaacs, A. C. and W. M. Carroll. "Strategies for Basic-Facts Instruction." *Teaching Children Mathematics* 5:9 (1999): 508-515.

Kouba, V. L. and K. Franklin. "Multiplication and Division: Sense Making and Meaning." *Research Ideas for the Classroom: Early Childhood Mathematics*. New York: Macmillan, 1993. 103-126.

Lamon, S. *Teaching Fractions and Ratios for Understanding*. Mahwah: Lawrence Erlbaum Associates, 1999.

Norton-Wolf, S. *Base-Ten Block Activities*. TK: Learning Resources, 1990.

Selected Research Bibliography

Rathmell, Edward C. "Using Thinking Strategies to Teach the Basic Facts." Ed. Marilyn N. Suydam. *Developing Computational Skills*. Reston: NCTM, 1978.

Saxe, G. B., M. Gearhart, and M. Seltzer. "Relations between Classroom Practices and Student Learning in the Domain of Fractions." *Cognition and Instruction* 17:1 (1999): 1-24.

Thornton, Carol A. and Paula J. Smith. "Action Research: Strategies for Learning Subtraction Facts." *Arithmetic Teacher* 35 (Apr 1988).

Trafton, P. and D. Thiesen. *Learning through Problems: Number Sense and Computational Strategies: A Resource for Teachers*. TK: Heinemann, 1999.

Trafton, P. R. and J. S Zawojewski. "Meaning of Operations." *Arithmetic Teacher* 38 (1990).

Wu, H. "Basic Skills Versus Conceptual Understanding: A Bogus Dichotomy in Mathematics Education." *American Educator* (Fall 1999).

Problem Solving

Chen, Z. "Children's Analogical Problem Solving: The Effects of Superficial, Structural, and Procedural Similarities." *Journal of Experimental Child Psychology* 62:3 (1996): 410-431.

Gick, M. L. and K. J. Holyoak. "Analogical Problem Solving." *Cognitive Psychology* 12 (1980): 306-355.

Hiebert, J. "Signposts for Teaching Mathematics through Problem Solving." Eds. F. K. Lester, Jr. and R. I. Charles. *Teaching Mathematics through Problem Solving*. Reston: National Council of Teachers of Mathematics, 2003. 53-61.

Schroeder, T. L. and F. K. Lester, Jr. "Developing Understanding in Mathematics via Problem Solving." *New Directions for Elementary School Mathematics*. Reston: National Council of Teachers of Mathematics, 1989.

Stanic, G. M. A. and J. Kilpatrick. "Historical Perspectives on Problem Solving in the Mathematics Curriculum." Eds. R. I. Charles and E. A. Silver. *The Teaching and Assessing of Mathematical Problem Solving*. Reston: National Council of Teacher of Mathematics, 1989. 1-22.

Suydam, M. N. "Untangling Clues from Research on Problem Solving." Eds. S. Krulik and R. E. Reys. *Problem Solving in School Mathematics: 1980 Yearbook*. Reston: National Council of Teachers of Mathematics, 1980. 43.

Reading & Writing

Blachowicz, C. L. Z. "Making Connections: Alternatives to the Vocabulary Notebook." *Journal of Reading* 29:2 (1986): 643-649.

Burton, Leone and Candia Morgan. "Mathematicians Writing" *Journal for Research in Mathematics Education* 31:4 (2000).

Carr, E. and D. Ogle. "K-W-L Plus: A Strategy for Comprehension and Summarization." *Journal of Reading* 30 (1987): 626-631.

Eanet, M. and A. Manzo. "R.E.A.P.--A Strategy for Improving Reading/Writing Study Skills." *Journal for Reading* 19 (1976): 647-652.

Martin, C. E., M. A. Martin, and D. G. O'Brien. "Spawning Ideas for Writing in the Content Area." *Reading World* 11 (1984): 11-15.

McGinley, W. and P. Denner. "Story Impressions: A Prereading/Writing Activity." *Journal of Reading* 31 (1987): 248-253.

McKeown, M., I. Beck, G. Sinatra, and J. Loxterman. "The Contribution of Prior Knowledge and Coherent Text to Comprehension." *Reading Research Quarterly* 27 (1992): 79-93.

Nagy, W. "On the Role of Context in First- and Second-language Vocabulary Learning." Eds. N. Schmitt and M. McCarthy. *Vocabulary: Description, Acquisition, and Pedagogy*. Cambridge, UK: Cambridge University Press, 1997. 64-83.

Palinscar, A.S. and A. Brown. "Interactive Teaching to Promote Independent Learning from Text." *Reading Teacher* 39:8 (1986): 771-777.

Siegel, M., R. Borasi, J. M. Fonzi, L. G. Sandridge, and C. Smith. "Using Reading to Construct Mathematical Meaning." Ed. P. C. Elliot. *Communication in Mathematics, K-12 and Beyond: 1996 Yearbook*. Reston: National Council of Teachers of Mathematics, 1996. 74.

Vygotsky, L. *Thought and Language*. Cambridge: MIT Press, 1962.

Whitin, David J. and Phyllis E.Whitin. "The 'Write' Way to Mathematical Understanding." Ed. Lorna J. Morrow. *Teaching and Learning of Algorithms in School Mathematics*. Reston: National Council of Teachers of Mathematics, Inc., 1998. 161-169.

Winograd, P. "Strategic Difficulties in Summarizing Texts." *Reading Research Quarterly* 19 (1984): 404-425.

National ESL Standards

GOAL 1 To use English to communicate in social settings

Standard 1:

Students will use English to interact and participate in social situations

   a. give and ask for information that communicates ideas
   b. share needs, feelings and thoughts
   c. employ body language and interpret nonverbal cues in social environments
   d. use communication to meet personal needs
   e. participate in discussions
   f. negotiate events and complete transactions

Standard 2:

Students will employ spoken and written English to express personal ideas, and demonstrate their inclusion in the English speaking environment

   a. discuss, join in or investigate activities of interest
   b. convey social and cultural ethics, traditions and norms
   c. communicate wants, thoughts and emotions
   d. take part in popular customs or traditions

Standard 3:

Students will use learned techniques to improve their ability to communicate in English

   a. investigate their theories of language use and structure
   b. mimic native speakers and listen attentively to how others use English
   c. think of other ways of saying things
   d. take notice and focus on specific sections and parts of language
   e. ask for assistance and assess feedback from others
   f. evaluate nonverbal and verbal cues
   g. monitor and appraise personal language development
   h. seek clarification in the primary language
   i. discover language "chunks" and use them appropriately
   j. choose varying forms of media to deepen comprehension
   k. attempt to speak, read, write and understand English
   l. apply context to help clarify meaning and build understanding

ESL Standards

GOAL 2 — To use English to achieve academically in all content areas

Standard 1:

Students will learn new content through communicating by speaking, reading and writing English in the classroom

- **a.** respond to implicit and explicit oral and written directions
- **b.** ask for and give explanations
- **c.** be involved in class, group and pair discussions
- **d.** pose and respond to questions
- **e.** ask for help and information as necessary
- **f.** handle interactions and bargain to complete assignments
- **g.** clarify actions
- **h.** broaden and expand on other's views and language
- **i.** communicate likes, dislikes, and needs

Standard 2:

Students will use English to acquire, sort out, create, and present content information in spoken and written forms

- **a.** compare and contrast information
- **b.** convince, debate, confer, assess, and defend ideas
- **c.** listen to, speak, read, and write about content
- **d.** assimilate information from oral and written forms
- **e.** retell information and sequences
- **f.** select, connect, and make information clear
- **g.** analyze, evaluate, synthesize, and infer ideas from various sources of information
- **h.** react to the work of peers and others
- **i.** represent and interpret information visually
- **j.** hypothesize and predict outcomes
- **k.** explore, create and ask questions to clarify ideas, information and content
- **l.** comprehend and generate procedural and academic vocabulary as well as text features specific to content areas
- **m.** display understanding by using and responding to language and content in multiple situations

Standard 3:

Students will use appropriate learning strategies to construct and apply academic knowledge

- **a.** pay attention to specific content information or language
- **b.** employ essential reading comprehension skills such as skimming, scanning, previewing, and revising text
- **c.** build meaning through context
- **d.** record key information (in first or second language) informally by taking notes and using them to remember ideas and linguistic information
- **e.** employ strategies that help construct and extend the knowledge base by monitoring and evaluating understanding, self-correcting as necessary

f. find out about and use techniques and environments that foster learning (e.g., when, where, how to study)

g. anticipate how and when to use cognitive strategies and use them appropriately during a learning task

h. vigorously connect new information to background knowledge

i. self-assess success and comprehension after finishing an assignment or task

j. identify situational learning needs and seek help from others (i.e.: teachers, classmates, other school professionals, family and community members)

k. mimic native English speakers behaviorally and linguistically to further internalize language

l. identify when first language and background knowledge applies to the learning environment and use it to deepen understanding

GOAL 3 To use English in socially and culturally appropriate ways

Standard 1:

Students will use the appropriate language variety, tone, formality and genre for the audience, purpose, and setting

a. change the degree of formality for different audiences and settings

b. Know and use standard English, colloquial speech and dialects appropriately

c. Use different writing styles for diverse audiences, purposes, and settings

d. use and react to slang properly

e. use and react to idioms properly

f. use and react to humor properly

g. decide when it is fitting to speak in a language other than English

h. understand which subjects are suitable for various social and learning situations

Standard 2:

Students will use nonverbal communication that suits the audience, intent, and environment

a. deduce and react properly to nonverbal cues and body language

b. demonstrate acceptable manners and suitable nonverbal classroom behaviors

c. vary the use of tone, volume, stress, and intonation as the situation demands

d. become aware of and adapt behavior in reaction to nonverbal signals

Standard 3:

Students will use new learning strategies to broaden their intercultural and linguistic competence

a. see and copy others speaking and behavior patterns of others in specific situations or settings

b. attempt adaptive language variations in various situations

c. continuously investigate and refine information about appropriate language use and behavior

d. determine the level of appropriateness of language use in various environments

e. evaluate language choices by what is most appropriate for the social context

f. practice variations of language in multiple settings

g. decide when slang use is appropriate

ESL Standards

Credits

Literature Credits

Cover of 10 FOR DINNER by Jo Ellen Bogart, Used with permission by Scholastic Inc. Canada All rights reserved.

100th DAY WORRIES Reprinted with the permission of Simon & Schuster Books for Young Readers, an imprint of Simon & Schuster Children's Publishing Division by Margery Cuyler, illustrated by Arthur Howard. Illustrations copyright © 2000 Arthur Howard.

26 LETTERS AND 99 CENTS Illustrations copyright © 1987 Tana Hoban. Used by permission of HarperCollins Publishers.

A FAIR BEAR SHARE COPYRIGHT © 1998 BY JOHN SPEIRS. Mathstart ™ is a Trademark of HarperCollins Publishers, Inc. Used by permission of HarperCollins Publishers.

A HOUSE FOR BIRDIE Illustrations copyright © 2004 by Edward Miller III. Mathstart ™ is a Trademark of HarperCollins Publishers, Inc. Used by permission of HarperCollins Publishers.

ALEXANDER, WHO USED TO BE RICH LAST SUNDAY Reprinted with the permission of Atheneum Books for Young Readers, an imprint of Simon & Schuster Children's Publishing Division by Judith Viorst, illustrated by Ray Cruz. Illustrations copyright © 1978 Ray Cruz.

Cover of ANIMAL GIANTS by Sara Louise Kras. Copyright © Kingfisher Publications Plc 2004. Reprinted by permission of Kingfisher Publications Plc, an imprint of Houghton Mifflin Company. All rights reserved.

APPLE FRACTIONS by Jerry Pallotta. Cover illustrations copyright © 2002. Reprinted by permission of Scholastic Inc.

Cover illustration by Martin Lemelman from BART'S AMAZING CHARTS by Diane Ochiltree. A Hello! Math Reader published by Cartwheel Books/Scholastic Inc. Copyright © 2001 by Scholastic Inc. Reprinted by permission.

BIGGER, BETTER, BEST! illustrations copyright © 2002 by Marsha Winborn. Mathstart ™ is a Trademark of HarperCollins Publishers, Inc. Used by permission of HarperCollins Publishers.

CAPTAIN INVINCIBLE AND THE SPACE SHAPES. Illustrations Copyright © 2001 by Remy Simard Used by permission of HarperCollins Publishers.

Cover illustration by Marcy Dunn Ramsaey from CATS ADD UP by Diane Ochiltree. A Hello! Math Reader published by Cartwheel Books/Scholastic Inc. Copyright © 1998 by Scholastic Inc. Reprinted by permission.

CIRCUS SHAPES ©1998 by R.W. Alley. Used by permission of HarperCollins Publishers.

Cover of COUNTING IS FOR THE BIRDS. Used with permission by Charlesbridge Publishing, Inc. All rights reserved.

COYOTES ALL AROUND by Stuart J. Murphy. Illustrations Copyright © 2003 by Steve Bjorkman. Mathstart ™ is a Trademark of HarperCollins Publishers, Inc. Used by permission of HarperCollins Publishers.

CUBES, CONES, CYLINDERS, AND SPHERES BY Tana Hoban. Used by permission of HarperCollins Publishers.

Cover of DOMINO ADDITION.Used with permission by Charlesbridge Publishing, Inc. All rights reserved.

DOUBLE THE DUCKS by Stuart J. Murphy. Illustrations Copyright © 2003 by Valeria Petrone. Used by permission of HarperCollins Publishers.

EACH ORANGE HAD 8 SLICES. Illustrations Copyright © 1992 by Donald Crews. Used by permission of HarperCollins Publishers.

EARTH-DAY HOORAY! Illustrations copyright © 2004 by Renee Adriani. Mathstart ™ is a Trademark of HarperCollins Publishers, Inc. Used by permission of HarperCollins Publishers.

From EATING FRACTIONS by Bruce McMillan. Copyright © 1991 by Bruce McMillan. Reprinted by permission for Scholastic Inc.

ELEVATOR MAGIC. COPYRIGHT © 1997 BY G. BRIAN KARAS. Mathstart ™ is a trademark of HarperCollins Publishers, Inc. Used by permission of HarperCollins Publishers.

EVERYBODY WINS! by Sheila Bruce and illustrated by Paige Billin-Frye. Copyright © 2001 by Kane Press, Inc. All rights reserved, including the right of reproduction in whole or in part in any form. This edition published by arrangement with Kane Press, Inc.

Special permission granted by Weekly Reader, Cover published and copyrighted by Weekly Reader Corporation. All rights reserved.

Cover of GOLD FEVER by Verla Kay, and illustrated by S.D. Schindler used with permission by Penguin Group (USA) Inc. All rights reserved.

Jacket cover by Robert Parker, copyright © 1990 by Robert Andrew Parker, from GRANDFATHER TANG'S STORY by Ann Tompert. Illustrated by Robert Andrew Parker. Used by permission of Crown Publishers, an imprint of Random House Children's Books, a division of Random House, Inc.

HENRY THE FOURTH. ILLUSTRATIONS COPYRIGHT © 1999 BY SCOTT NASH. Used by permission of HarperCollins Publishers.

From HOW BIG IS A FOOT? Jacket Cover by Rolf Myller, copyright © 1962, renewed 1990 by Rolf Myller. Used by permission of Bantam Books, a division of Random House, Inc.

Cover of HOW BIG WERE THE DINOSAURS? by Bernard Most used with permission by Harcourt Brace & Company. All rights reserved.

Illustration by Meredith Johnson from HOW MUCH IS THAT GUINEA PIG IN THE WINDOW? By Joanne Rocklin. A Hello! Math Reader published by Cartwheel Books/Scholastic Inc. Copyright © 1995 by Scholastic Inc. Reprinted by permission.

Illustration copyright © 2005 by James Warhola from IF DOGS WERE DINOSAURS by David Schwartz. Reprinted by permission of Scholastic Inc.

Cover from INCHWORM AND A HALF by Elinor J. Pinczes, illustrated by Randall Enos. Reprinted by permission of Houghton Mifflin Company. All rights reserved.

From JELLY BEANS FOR SALE by Bruce McMillan. Copyright © 1996 by Bruce McMillan. Reprinted by permission of Scholastic Inc.

JUMP, KANGAROO, JUMP COPYRIGHT © 1999 BY KEVIN O'MALLEY. Mathstart ™ is a trademark of HarperCollins Publishers, Inc. Used by permission of HarperCollins Publishers.

JUST ENOUGH CARROTS. Illustrations copyright © 1997 by Frank Remkiewicz. Mathstart ™ is a Trademark of HarperCollins Publishers, Inc. Used by permission of HarperCollins Publishers.

LEMONADE FOR SALE Copyright © 1998 BY Tricia Tusa Mathstart ™ is a trademark of HarperCollins Publishers, Inc. Used by permission of HarperCollins Publishers.

LESS THAN ZERO by Stuart J. Murphy. Illustrations copyright © 2003 by Frank Remkiewicz. Used by permission of HarperCollins Publishers.

MALL MANIA. Illustrations copyright © 2006 by Renee Andriani. Mathstart ™ is a Trademark of HarperCollins Publishers, Inc. Used by permission of HarperCollins Publishers.

Illustration by Heather Cahoon from MATH FABLES by Greg Tang. Scholastic Inc./ Scholastic Press. Jacket art copyright © 2004 by Scholastic Inc. Reprinted by permission.

Cover of MATH MINI-MYSTERIES by Sandra Markle. Used with permission Sandra Markle. All rights reserved.

Cover of MEASURING PENNY written and illustrated by Loreen Leedy. Copyright © 1998 by Loreen Leedy. Reprinted by permission of Henry Holt and Company, LLC

MONSTER MUSICAL CHAIRS. Illustrations copyright © 2000 by Scott Nash. Mathstart ™ is a Trademark of HarperCollins Publishers, Inc. Used by permission of HarperCollins Publishers.

MORE OR LESS? Illustrations copyright © 2005 by David Wenzel. Mathstart ™ is a Trademark of HarperCollins Publishers, Inc. Used by permission of HarperCollins Publishers.

ONE DUCK STUCK. Text copyright © 1998 by Phyllis Root. Illustrations © 1998 by Jane Chapman. Reproduced by permission of Candlewick Press, Cambridge, MA.

Cover from ONE HUNDRED HUNGRY ANTS by Elinor J. Pinczes, illustrated by Bonnie MacKain. Jacket cover copyright © 1993 by Bonnie MacKain. Reprinted by permission of Houghton Mifflin Company. All rights reserved.

Credits

Photo Credits

Anthology Credits

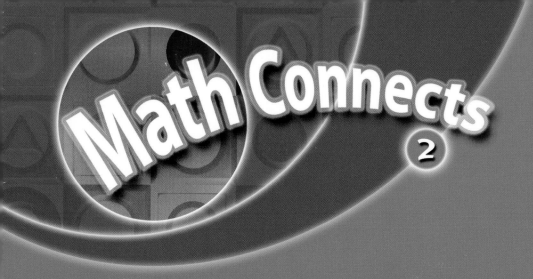

Math Connects 2

Contents

The *McGraw·Hill* Companies

Math Online > macmillanmh.com

ISBN: 978-0-02-107523-2
MHID: 0-02-107523-9

90000

9 780021 075232

**Macmillan/McGraw-Hill
Glencoe**